# Heat
# Pumps

# HEAT PUMPS

## SECOND EDITION

### R. D. Heap

SHIPOWNERS REFRIGERATED CARGO
RESEARCH ASSOCIATION, CAMBRIDGE, UK

LONDON     NEW YORK

E. & F. N. SPON

*First published 1979 by*
*E. & F. N. Spon Ltd*
*11 New Fetter Lane, London EC4P 4EE*

*Second edition 1983*
*Published in the USA by*
*E. & F. N. Spon*
*733 Third Avenue, New York NY 10017*

© *1979, 1983 R. D. Heap*

*Phototypeset by Sunrise Setting, Torquay*
*Printed in Great Britain by*
*J. W. Arrowsmith Ltd, Bristol*

ISBN 0 419 12600 7

**British Library Cataloguing in Publication Data**

Heap, R. D.
  Heat pumps.
  1.  Heat pumps
  I.  Title
  621.402′5          TJ262

  ISBN 0-419-12600-7


**Library of Congress Cataloging in Publication Data**

Heap, R. D.
  Heat pumps.
  Bibliography:p.
  Includes index.
  1.  Heat pumps.     I.  Title
TH7638.H42          1983          697′.07          83-12418
ISBN 0-419-12600-7

# Contents

# Preface to first edition

Energy is a fundamental requirement for an industrialized society and many traditional sources of energy have limited lifetimes. Considerable effort is being devoted to finding new sources and to making better use of the available supplies.

Heat pumps are sometimes thought of as energy sources along with solar panels and windmills, but heat pumps use energy even though they often use less energy than alternative equipment. There is, therefore, a great deal of interest in heat pumps, and many applications are technically feasible, although at present only a few are economically worthwhile. With increasing energy costs and changing cost relativities, many potential applications deserve frequent reassessment and it is the aim of this book to assist potential designers, specifiers, suppliers, installers, and users of heat pumps to carry out such reassessments.

I have written this book with the heat pump specifier in mind, be he architect, services engineer, or potential purchaser, and I have assumed that the reader is familiar with the basic concepts of temperature, heat, and energy (if in doubt one of the thermodynamics textbooks in the bibliography should be consulted). As I am neither a thermodynamicist nor a refrigeration engineer it would be impertinent and unwise for me to intrude too far into the realms of basic theory and equipment design, although I have aimed for sufficient detail to enable the specifier to understand the various options which may be considered and their relevance to the systems in which they may be used. If the equipment designer finds the book a useful checklist, so much the better.

Domestic applications are considered before applications in commercial buildings and in industry, as they are generally more straightforward and to some extent the principles are applicable in all three areas. This order has been chosen to minimize the necessary duplication of common material and, while it may also reflect the bias of my personal experience, it is not intended to suggest an order of either the importance or the value of heat pump applications.

The first two chapters include general, historical and theoretical background material, Chapter 3 considers vapour compression equipment in some detail, and Chapter 4 considers general aspects of system design, with special reference to the design of space-heating systems using heat pumps. Chapters 5–7 cover domestic, commercial and industrial applications respectively, and Chapter 8 considers the relevance of some methods of economic analysis to the selection of heat pump systems. Throughout the book, the terms 'economic' (meaning profitable by comparison with alternative investments) and 'worthwhile' (a more subjective value-judgement) will be used somewhat loosely, as a rigorous assessment may depend on the assessor as much as on the application.

Vapour compression machinery as used in most heat pumps is complex, particularly in the way in which the components interact, and it is fortunate that it has been highly developed for the refrigeration industry. The description of this equipment in Chapter 3 will be familiar to the refrigeration engineer but has been included for the many other readers who will wish to have a fuller understanding of how it works.

Further details on all aspects of refrigeration engineering are readily available, the most comprehensive and detailed source being the series of handbooks produced and updated regularly by the American Society of Heating, Refrigeration, and Air-Conditioning Engineers (ASHRAE). The term 'air-conditioning', which strictly means simultaneous control of temperature, humidity, and cleanliness of air supplies, is frequently used loosely to mean 'air-cooling', and in referring in this book to equipment which could be used either for cooling or for air-conditioning, it has not proved practicable to adhere to the strict definition.

S.I. (Système Internationale d'Unites) units are used throughout the book, although the compound unit, kilowatt-hour (kWh) is used for energy rather than a multiple of the joule, wherever it is thought that this will be more readily understood.

References to published work are given in the text as they arise and will enable the student or researcher to find out more about particular topics. Those references are listed numerically at the end of each chapter. A general bibliography of textbooks, equipment guides, literature surveys, and journals is given separately at the end of the book. It must be noted that the inclusion of any idea in this book does not imply that it is free from patent protection or may be freely used.

**Acknowledgements**

I wish to acknowledge the assistance and encouragement given to me by my employers, the Electricity Council, and to thank the Director of the Research Centre, Dr A. T. Churchman, and all my colleagues both at

Capenhurst and in London who have contributed ideas and useful criticism. The opinions expressed in this book are my own and do not necessarily represent the views or policies of my employers. A book of this nature is inevitably incomplete, but if there are any errors or misleading implications in the text, I would be pleased to have them drawn to my attention.

I must thank those manufacturers and others who have kindly supplied material for figures and who are acknowledged in the figure captions. Special thanks must go to Joan Hughes for preparation of the manuscript, and to my wife Wendy, who not only provided support and sustenance but also edited successive drafts and prepared the references.

*Ellesmere Port*                                                               R. D. H.
*July 1978*

# Preface to second edition

Four years is not a long time in the history of heat pumps and their applications. The years from 1978 to 1982 have seen rapid development of heat pump markets, considerable research into 'advanced' heat pump systems, and appreciable development of standards and specifications. All these, and many other smaller topics, have been taken into account in revising *Heat Pumps* for this second edition.

A new section on sales has been incorporated in Chapter 1, and the research section has been expanded. More has been included in Chapter 2 on absorption cycles and on possible refrigerants.

Chapter 3 incorporates recent information on choice of refrigerants for high-temperature applications, and up to date information on the chloro-fluorocarbon safety debate. There is an expanded section on compressor drives and choice of fuel, reflecting the increased interest in engine-driven heat pumps. Information on single screw compressors is added, there is more data on reliability and the standards section has been extended and fully revised.

There are only minor alterations to Chapter 4, but Chapter 5 has been completely restructured to incorporate recent developments, including a new section on gas-fired units. Details of small prototype electric heating-only units are given.

Chapters 6 and 7 incorporate more recent and varied examples of installations, some new systems, and a new section on industrial fuel-fired heat pumps. Chapter 8 has only minor changes. The Bibliography has been revised and completely updated.

I hope that the amendments have not only answered the encouragingly small amount of adverse criticism of the first edition but have also improved the balance of the book as a whole.

I parted company with the Electricity Council in 1979 after twelve years at their Research Centre, and am now employed as Principal Research Officer at Shipowners Refrigerated Cargo Research Association, Cambridge.

*Stapleford, Cambridge*                                     R. D. H.
*September 1982*

# Introduction

## 1.1 Definitions

A heat pump is a device which extracts heat energy from a source at a low temperature and makes it available as useful heat energy at a higher temperature. This implies that there is some planned use for the higher temperature heat energy, thus distinguishing heat pumps from otherwise similar refrigerating and air-conditioning equipment in which the higher temperature energy is rejected as waste. The boundaries between heat recovery, heat pumping and air-conditioning are not always well-defined. Only those heat recovery situations in which the recovered heat is upgraded in temperature may be regarded as heat pump applications. Air-conditioning is only relevant to heat pumping when it provides a source of heat which is usefully applied. Two simple examples of heat pump applications are pumping heat from cooling water to provide space heating in a factory, and pumping heat from outdoor air to heat houses or small shops. Such applications can be worthwhile because the amount of energy required to operate the heat pump is only a fraction of the total heating energy provided.

The essential components of any heat pump are the heat exchangers through which heat energy is extracted and made available (Fig. 1.1). Various means of pumping heat between these exchangers are described in Chapter 2, including vapour compression, refrigeration cycles, chemical absorption, gas compression, and thermoelectric methods. All these have in common a need for an energy input (mechanical, electrical, or thermal) to make them operate.

The ratio of energy made available ($E$) to operating energy input ($q$) is the basic measure of the effectiveness of a heat pump. This ratio is variously known as 'coefficient of performance', 'coefficient of heating', 'reciprocal thermal efficiency', 'performance ratio', or 'performance energy ratio'. The most widely used term is 'coefficient of performance', conveniently abbreviated to 'c.o.p'. This is often used with a subscript 'h' (for 'heating') to distinguish it from the similarly named term defined for cooling equipment

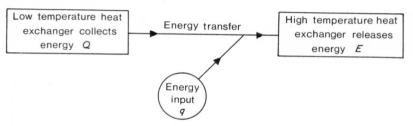

*Fig. 1.1* The basic heat pump concept.

as the ratio of cooling effect ($Q$) to energy input, i.e. $Q/q$. Generally, in this book 'c.o.p.' will be used to mean $E/q$, the ratio of heat energy made available to total energy input for operating the equipment. To be effective a heat pump must have a c.o.p. in excess of unity and the higher the c.o.p. the more effective it will be. Values of 5 or 6 are feasible with large machines pumping through small temperature differences, and even small machines using outdoor air as a source can have a c.o.p. between 2 and 3.

### 1.2 Economics

Heat pumps are effective in energy terms but they are not widely used. The main reason for this is their high capital cost compared with that of established alternatives. For any particular application the heat pump must be evaluated by comparing it with other systems to see if it offers an economic advantage. The evaluation must allow for the differing efficiencies of alternative systems using different fuels and for total costs, including capital and maintenance charges.

Frequently, alternative systems will be better known and cheaper, so that heat pump energy savings need to be balanced against higher capital costs and uncertain maintenance costs. Conventional analysis will show that some heat pump applications are clearly economic, but in many cases there will be uncertainties requiring a broader judgement. Some thoughts about the economic analysis of energy saving schemes will be found in Chapter 8, where a simple method for ranking different energy-saving schemes is proposed.

Whenever economic factors relating to energy supply are changing rapidly, the viable range of heat pump applications has been reassessed, and with each increase in fuel costs, this range has been increased. Manufacturers' predictions and national surveys both point to a rapid increase in heat pump sales in the 1980s, and this is likely as long as energy costs increase faster than wealth. It remains to be seen whether this will make the last quarter of the 20th century a period when the heat pump plays a significant part in national energy economies or whether heat pumps will be overtaken by other technologies which reduce heating requirements. In either case there will be a continuing need to assess realistically the viability of heat pumping. Appreciation of the historical background is a protection against the twin dangers of excessive enthusiasm for apparent novelty and of undue scepticism for a concept for which worthwhile applications have been slow in developing.

## 1.3 History

The growth in understanding of physical processes in the 19th century led to interest in the possibility of pumping heat energy to a higher temperature. Joule demonstrated the principle of changing the temperature of a gas by altering its pressure, and Professor Piazzi Smythe was one of the first to propose a cooling machine using this principle. Professor Thomson (later to be Lord Kelvin) was the first to propose the heat pump.

Thomson [1] published a paper in 1852 describing a system in which, using a linked compressor and expander, air was moved to and from a reservoir which also acted as a heat exchanger. This open cycle unit could be used for either heating or cooling buildings. In his paper Thomson foresaw the closed cycle vapour compression machine, but neither the refrigerants nor the drive motors were available to enable him to design anything really resembling the modern heat pump. Although Thomson is an important figure in heat pump history, the heat pump idea was only a minor part of his very considerable scientific output [2].

Development of refrigeration equipment using these ideas progressed rapidly in the 1870s, a number of cold-air refrigeration machines being produced in response to the needs of the international frozen meat trade. By 1879, Bell-Coleman of Glasgow had installed equipment in ships bringing meat to Britain from both the US and Australia [3]. At the same time, work was in progress developing vapour compression machines for the future, using ether, ammonia, or methyl chloride as refrigerants. The cold-air refrigeration machines were ousted by carbon dioxide machines, and by the 1920s ammonia compression had become established. Smaller refrigeration equipment changed to methyl chloride in the 1930s, and by the early 1940s the first of the modern halocarbon refrigerants, R12, was available [4,5].

The history of the development of refrigeration has been fully surveyed by Thévenot [6], specific details of compressor history have been described by Newton [7] and some interesting early absorption systems are considered by Higham [8].

Over this period of refrigeration equipment development, the development of heat pumps lagged behind. While refrigeration met an established need, heat pump development depended on energy costs and availability and on the alternative heat generators available. The development of heat

## 4  Heat pumps

pumps themselves parallels the development of refrigeration equipment – it is in the application of heat pumps that particular interest lies and from which lessons for the future may be learned.

First heat pump applications were considered in the 1920s, with restatements of and improvements on Thomson's paper by Krauss [9] and Morley [10], and although there were no heat pumps as such in existence it was possible to examine their feasibility from analysis of the performance of the rapidly increasing amount of refrigeration equipment which was being installed. This was done by Haldane [11], who analysed data from a selection of refrigerating plant operating between 1891 and 1926. He produced a graph of obtainable c.o.p. related to heat output temperatures (Fig. 1.2), showing this to be one-third to one-half of the theoretical efficiency of a reverse Carnot engine, which is described in Section 2.2.

From these results, Haldane was able to recommend that reversible heat pumps to provide cooling and heating of buildings should be considered, and to illustrate the particularly attractive economics of heat pump applications for energy recovery in swimming bath halls. Although equipment is improved and prices have changed, these proposals remain sound to the present day.

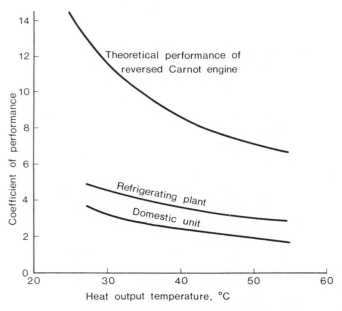

*Fig. 1.2* Heat pump performance, as determined by Haldane for 4.4°C source temperature (−6.7 °C evaporation temperature).

Not content with theoretical calculations, Haldane constructed an experimental heat pump in the mid 1920s to provide space heating and water heating in his home in Scotland. He used both outdoor air and mains water as heat sources, a low temperature hot-water radiator heat-distribution system, and an electrically driven refrigeration compressor. The refrigerant was ammonia. The electricity supply came from a localized hydroelectric generator, giving an installation which would not look amiss at a present day alternative technology exhibition. The performance of the domestic unit was not as good as that calculated for the larger refrigeration equipment (Fig. 1.2), but it showed a worthwhile c.o.p. and, apart from a 'little' noise difficulty, appears to have been effective.

Probably the first large-scale heat pump application was in the Los Angeles offices of the Southern California Edison Company [12] where in 1930–31 refrigerating equipment was used for heating purposes. A c.o.p. of between 1.45 and 1.98 was obtained, although a figure of 2.32 was considered possible under the most favourable operating conditions.

The economic difficulties of the 1930s provided the necessary spur for heat pump development in Europe, and an appreciable number of large-scale applications were in existence by 1943, when the journal *Electrical Service* issued a special report [13] on 'Energy economy and the thermodynamic heat pump'. Possible applications which were listed included evaporation heat pumps using the latent heat of vapours in condensation processes, industrial waste heat recovery, and air or water source units for space heating. The use of a steam-turbine-driven heat pump utilizing turbine waste heat was also proposed. At that time heat pumping in processes involving the concentration of liquids was considered economic, but the recovery of waste heat in other applications was only considered worthwhile if the recovered heat was produced by cooling equipment.

Ready availability of hydroelectricity in Switzerland favoured the electrically driven heat pump, and installations at the Zurich Council Hall, Congress Hall, and Swimming Hall in the 1937–41 period were among those described. Heat pumps in a school, a hospital, offices and a dairy are also referred to, and a bibliography [14] of 55 references covered the period from 1922–1943. Fifteen commercial applications installed by 1940 in the United States are listed by Kemler and Oglesby [15], the majority using well water as their heat source.

Some of the early heat pumps continued in service for many years; for example, a water source unit in a bank in Milan, Italy, designed in 1935 as an ammonia unit was still running and converted to use a fluorocarbon refrigerant in 1971.

In the United States, development of smaller heat pump units, basically reversible air-conditioners for domestic use providing either heating or cooling, had progressed sufficiently by 1948 for a field test procedure [16] to be formulated and for field tests to be performed by electricity supply utilities [17]. Possible problems of electricity demand characteristics were examined closely and the dangers of excessive heat losses from air distribution ductwork were noted.

Around 1950 work was done in both the United States and Britain on domestic heat pumps using ground coils as a heat source. Baker [18] designed a reversible unit incorporating an antifreeze storage bath, and reported a c.o.p. of over 3 on average over the winter of 1950–51. Sumner [19] installed a ground-source heat pump to heat his home, and Griffith [20] at the Electrical Research Association started research into properties of and heat transfer from soil.

The first large-scale heat pump in Britain was designed by Sumner [21] as an experimental machine to heat a block of municipal buildings in Norwich. This machine came into operation in 1945 and was dismantled after a few years' use. In its final form it used a two-stage compressor and sulphur dioxide refrigerant, had a design output of approximately 240 kW, and used adjacent river water as a heat source. A c.o.p. of between 3 and 4 was calculated, the average achieved over the heating season being nearer to the higher figure.

An experimental unit was designed for the Festival Hall to be built in London for the 1951 exhibition. This was an ambitious experiment [22] which has been the subject of frequent misunderstanding and which deserves further description. The unit used the River Thames as a heat source and was operated with town gas and designed to give a heat output of 2.3–2.6 MW. The high-speed centrifugal compressors were the converted superchargers of the modified Merlin aircraft engines which drove them, and there was a two-stage refrigerant cycle with inter-stage vapour fed back to the second compressor for improved efficiency (see page 21). The refrigerant was R12, and single-stage cooling operation was also incorporated. There were difficulties with refrigerant flow control and with seals but a c.o.p. of 2.5–3 was obtained when supplying water at 82°C to the heating system, with an evaporating temperature of 0°C. Unfortunately, the Festival Hall experimental unit had a very limited use, due principally to its output being excessive relative to the heat demand from the Hall, and for this reason the more advantageous aspects of the experiment have sometimes been ignored.

A very different type of heat pump was developed in Britain around 1954 – the Ferranti Fridge-Heater [23,24] (Fig. 1.3). This was a domestic unit designed to extract heat from a food storage room and use it to heat water. The unit was small, with a heat output of 1.2 kW in summer and 0.7 kW in winter, but it failed to find a substantial market despite its simplicity and its low costs. However, small commercial machines of a similar type were developed and successfully used in ice cream parlours, in which heat from the freezer was used to provide hot water for the sink.

In the early 1960s reversible domestic air-to-air heat pumps established an appreciable sales success in the United States. Unfortunately they also established a poor reputation for reliability, as it had not been fully appreciated that reversible heat pumps need to be more than just an air conditioner with a refrigerant flow reversing valve added. By 1964, reliability problems were sufficiently severe for US military authorities to ban heat pumps from military housing, a ban which lasted until 1975 [25]. In response to these reliability problems, the Edison Electric Institute encouraged manufacturers to produce improved units for both residential and commercial use, and also monitored the reliability of the improved units in detail [26]. Improved compressors able to withstand the lubrication and cooling problems associated with reversing the cycle were produced, and new operating cycles were devised.

*Fig. 1.3* The Ferranti Fridge-Heater.

## 8   Heat pumps

The growth of production of electric air-to-air heat pumps in the US is shown in Fig. 1.4. Virtually all these units are designed as reversible air-conditioners. Early sales were mostly for commercial premises but residential units were in the majority by 1960. The recession accompanying the oil price rise in the early 1970s led to an immediate fall in commercial applications but by 1975 this sector had recovered and the residential sector had started on a period of rapid growth, peaking in 1978. It would be reasonable to expect production to settle at around 400 000–500 000 units per annum, perhaps with a small, steady growth, though manufacturers are more optimistic, predicting a further doubling through the 1980s [27].

Following American developments, heat pump applications increased worldwide in the late 1960s and early 1970s. Small, domestic units using outdoor air as a heat source were produced (notably in Japan [28], Sweden [29] and France [30]), and larger units were increasingly incorporated into integrated heat-recovery designs for larger commercial and public buildings, particularly in the United Kingdom [31] and in Germany [32]. Many of the smaller units were reversible for applications with appreciable cooling loads.

Following the oil price increases of the early 1970s, heat pump applications where cooling was not required began to become economically more attractive and national energy use surveys in Britain and Sweden [33, 34] showed how heat pumping could reduce domestic space-heating energy

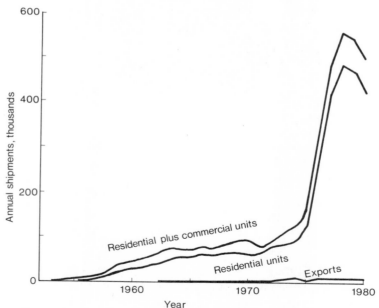

*Fig. 1.4* Annual production of electric air-to-air heat pumps in the USA.

requirements economically. The suitability of the well-established reversible equipment for this new role was questioned in Britain [35], and studies were implemented [36] to show the gains in efficiency which could be obtained by designing specifically for heating applications. In the interests of energy conservation, development started on non-electric heat pumps operating directly from the combustion of fuel, and it is possible that such equipment, using a gas-fired Stirling engine, could be marketed in the United States in the not-too-distant future [37].

## 1.4 Sales

The sales of packaged heat pumps in the US are well documented and there is no difficulty in observing sales trends but in other countries data are more difficult to obtain and where available may be on differing bases. Heat pumps may be classified as refrigeration plant or heat recovery equipment and thus not specifically identified. Nevertheless the figures below, based on a variety of sources, can be taken as indicative of sales levels of some particular types of unit in particular countries but cannot be guaranteed to be completely accurate or comprehensive.

*USA:* air-to-air reversible units selling at a rate of 500 000 per year in 1981, a total of 4 million produced (see Fig. 1.4).

*France:* 23 000 units installed in 1981, mostly air to air in 'collective' dwellings, but including a substantial number of timber-drying dehumidifiers.

*West Germany:* sales of 30 000 in 1980, many being small units but including about 500 larger than 50 kW. About 1% of the total were diesel or gas driven. Production exceeded sales by over 50% in 1980 due to over-optimistic forecasts.

*UK:* domestic installations were about 500 in 1981, commercial installations about 2000. At present no comprehensive statistical records are available but the market is increasing steadily in all sectors.

*Denmark:* about 2000 units installed by 1980.

*Japan:* the main production is reversible room air- conditioning units, of which 750 000 were produced in 1980/81.

*Sweden:* about 5000 space-heating heat pumps of less than 15 kW output were installed by 1980.

One major Swedish-based manufacturer advertises a range of heat pumps with heating duties from 20 to 7500 kW using reciprocating compressors up to about 600 kW and screw compressors for larger sizes. Electric drive is normal but gas or diesel drives are available when the recovered engine heat can make the extra capital and maintenance costs worth while. A unit of around 1 MW output is shown in Fig. 1.5.

Output temperature ranges are 40–55°C with R22 or R502 refrigerants,

*Fig. 1.5* A screw compressor heat pump unit of approximately 1 MW capacity. Courtesy of Stal-Levin Ltd.

55–70°C with R12, and 70–110°C with R114 but the higher temperature R114 range is relatively unproved as yet. An analysis of 75 systems installed in the period 1976 to 1981 is given in Table 1.1, most of these being in Swedish industrial applications. A combination of relatively low electricity costs and government subsidies makes some of these installations particularly worth while but even without these many would show quite short payback times [38].

The range of larger applications is well illustrated by representative examples in Switzerland which include a district heating scheme, office buildings associated with a road tunnel, a sports centre, a knife factory, and a proposal to use industrial waste heat to warm local schools [39].

As can be seen from figures above, apart from a few large units the sales of heat pumps in Europe were negligible up to the early 1970s, whereas by 1980 around 100 000 small commercial or residential units had been installed. This quantity is substantial, representing a power demand of perhaps 700 MW, but still represents a very small proportion of all heating systems.

## 1.5 Research and development

The fuel price increases in the early 1970s also led to anxieties about future

*Table 1.1* Analysis of 75 installations by a Swedish-based manufacturer, 1976–81 [38]

| | |
|---|---|
| *Analysis by unit size* | |
| Less than 100 kW heat output | 20% |
| 100–199 kW | 34% |
| 200–399 kW | 16% |
| 400–800 kW | 12% |
| Over 800 kW | 18% |
| *Analysis by heat source (several units have multiple sources)* | |
| Air | |
| outdoor | 9% |
| other | 15% |
| Water | |
| sewage | 16% |
| waste | 20% |
| river | 4% |
| lake | 5% |
| sea | 4% |
| Soil | 12% |
| Other | 28% |
| *Analysis by heat use* | |
| Local space heating | 83% |
| District heating | 8% |
| Process heating | 7% |
| Water heating | 31% |
| Other | 1% |

energy supplies and to a rapid growth of interest in heat pump research. Established manufacturers have looked for expanding market areas, new manufacturers have appeared, and both practical development and basic research have flourished. Developments have included new compressors, new heat-exchange surfaces, and improved control systems, and have led to improved performance and better reliability, but there has also been a crop of enthusiastically promoted ideas varying from the ineffective to the thermodynamically impossible.

In the basic research field, new refrigerants and new operating cycles are being assessed by universities, manufacturers, utilities, and others. There is often an overlap between research programmes at different institutions, but this is not necessarily a bad thing as long as it leads to reinforcement of common findings and to increased awareness of where development work is necessary. Economic assessments to determine the most suitable heat pump specifications for particular applications have been completed in a number of countries, leading to suggestions for future equipment development. Carefully monitored field trials of equipment have been encouraged, so that the practical benefits of heat pumps can be properly assessed.

Progress in heat pump research and development is being monitored by international organizations concerned with energy supplies, including the World Energy Conference (WEC), the International Energy Agency (IEA), and the Scientific and Technical Research Committee of the European Community (EEC–CREST). IEA work has recently been summarized in detail by Hodgett and Oelert [40]. The International Council for Building Research Studies and Documentation (CIB) publishes reviews of current research, including that into heat pumps applied to buildings, and the International Institute of Refrigeration (IIR) includes work on a wide range of heat pump applications in its publications.

Heat pumps of all types are probably used more widely in the United States than in any other country, and the combined efforts of manufacturers, utilities, universities and government result in current research into nearly every aspect of heat pump development and use. A survey in 1978 highlighted amongst other things a need for units designed to fit into existing houses in place of existing systems, a need for reliability monitoring and setting of standards, and a possibility of duplication of work on mixed systems such as those combining heat pumps and solar heating [41]. More recent reviews and assessments suggest that the US Department of Energy has by now completed enough work to be able to evaluate any possible combination of solar heating with heat pumps [42, 43].

The main US project concerned with improving existing systems rather than developing new ones has been sponsored by the Electric Power Research Institute who have identified areas for improvement and have gone ahead with an $11.7 million, 4.5 years project to produce improved units for trials starting in 1983 and 1984 [44]. Recent developments of the heat pump water heater and current development of gas-fired heat pump units could have considerable effects on future markets. Research in Canada with emphasis on improved designs for northern climates has been mainly sponsored by Ontario Hydro who have undertaken a number of projects since 1976.

In Europe a wide range of energy conservation projects was sponsored by ,the EEC over the period 1975–9, and a new series of projects over the period 1979–83 followed [45–47]. The first series of over 100 projects included about 20 heat pump projects over a wide range of areas. The second series of about 150 projects includes 31 relating to heat pumps, the majority of which relate to either absorption or advanced engine-driven systems.

In Britain work on electric heat pumps includes the assessment of domestic air-to-water units for existing houses (an Electricity Council project with some government support), and continuing efforts to develop and expand the market for high-temperature heat pumps and industrial driers. Gas-fired units for industrial use have reached the demonstration project stage and smaller gas-fired units for domestic use (mostly using absorption cycles) are being actively developed by British Gas with a view to their use in the late 1980s. There are a number of research projects at universities and polytechnics but overall there is a conspicuous lack of central co-ordination or funding of the type which has been seen in the US [48, 49].

In Germany published papers reflect a continuing interest in alternative thermodynamic cycles and working fluids. Air-to-water and water-to-water domestic units have been developed to production levels which have become a problem both because of anxieties about water extraction and the environment and because of over-optimistic sales forecasts. Such problems are not conducive to increased research funding, but work in progress includes a considerable programme at Battelle-Institut e.V., Frankfurt, including development and assessment of absorption heat pumps, heat pumps for district heating and for industry, and evaluation of working media for alternative cycles.

In France, Eléctricité de France (EdF) continues to sponsor investigations into new heat pump applications and to develop substantial markets. In a number of European countries such as the Netherlands fuel prices and availability favour the use of natural gas and this is reflected in EEC research projects referred to above. A great deal of heat pump research has taken place in Sweden mainly sponsored through the Swedish Council for Building Research, much of it related to heat extraction from ground or water sources [50, 51].

Research is active in many other countries and details for any particular country may be obtained by locating national representatives of the international organizations mentioned previously (WEC, IEA, EEC, CIB and IIR). Research in Russia and developments in Bulgaria have been outlined in published papers [52, 53].

Particularly relevant items of research will be referred to in this book as they arise. Most research results are published in readily available technical and scientific journals the most relevant of which are listed in the bibliography.

The development of new equipment and the improved matching of equipment to the particular climatic and economic needs of particular countries should continue to extend the range of worthwhile heat pump applications. However, there are areas of concern in heat pump development. There is a continuing failure to appreciate that systems which it can be argued are marginally economic can rarely be made more attractive by added complexity. There are too many large research projects concluding that, 'the system examined, while theoretically attractive, is not likely to be economically worthwhile in the foreseeable future', or words to that effect. Such projects are draining enthusiasm and resources which would be better used improving the engineering and reliability of existing heat pump systems. Another concern is the ever-growing number of heat pump patents both for specific applications of known techniques and for trivial modifications to established systems. Such patents add little to heat pump technology and could have a restricting influence on future designs.

These problems can be attributed to an insufficiently wide understanding of the operation and application of heat pumping techniques and to an incomplete appreciation of the ways in which heat energy is used. There can be no doubt that heat pumps can make a real contribution to intelligent energy management in the coming decades, but that contribution can only reach its full potential if there are sufficient people available with the right education and training to develop it.

## References

[1] Thomson, W. (1852). 'On the economy of the heating or cooling of buildings by means of currents of air'. *Glasgow Phil. Soc. Proc.* 269–72.
[2] Thompson, S.P. (1910). *Life of Lord Kelvin.* (2 Vols.), Macmillan, London.
[3] Coleman, J.J. (1882). 'Air refrigerating machinery and its applications'. *Proc. Inst. Civil Engrs.* **68**, 146–70, discussion 170–215.
[4] Jordan, R.C. and Priester, G.B. (1956). *Refrigeration and air conditioning,* 2nd edn. Constable, London.
[5] Fearon, J. (1978). 'The history and development of the heat pump'. *Refrigeration and Air Conditioning* **81** (961), 79–99.
[6] Thevenot, R. (translated by Fidler, J.C.) (1979). *A history of refrigeration throughout the world.* International Institute of Refrigeration, Paris.
[7] Newton, A.B. (1981). 'The refrigeration compressor – the steps to maturity'. *Int. J. Refrig.* **4** (5), 246–54.
[8] Higham, D.W. (1981). 'The absorption systems of Eugene Dominique Nicolle (1823–1909) Innovator and Engineer extraordinary.' *Proc. Inst. Refrig.* **77**, 40–7.
[9] Krauss, F. (1921). 'The heat pump in theory and practice'. *Power* **54**, 298–300.
[10] Morley, T.B. (1922). 'The reversed heat engine as a means of heating buildings'. *The Engineer* 10 February, 145–6.
[11] Haldane, T.G.N. (1930). 'The heat pump – an economical method of producing low-grade heat from electricity'. *J.I.E.E.E.* 666–75
[12] Doolittle, H.L. (1932). 'Heating with refrigerating equipment cuts current costs'. *Power* **76**, 29–31.
[13] Anon. (1944). 'Energy economy and the thermodynamic heat pump'. *Electrical Service* 1943/44 (7–9), 116–85.
[14] *ibid,* p. 185.
[15] Kemler, E.N. and Oglesby, S. (1950). *Heat pump applications* McGraw-Hill, New York.
[16] Joint AEIC-EEI heat pump committee (1948), 'Suggested field test procedure for determination of coefficient of performance and performance factor of an electric heat pump while operating on the heating cycle'. *Edison Electric Inst. Bull.* **16**, 341–8.

[17] Sporn, P. and Ambrose, E.R. (1951). 'Tests show how heat pumps perform in different climates'. *Electrical World* **135**, (4), 97–100.

[18] Baker, M. (1953). 'Design and performance of a residential earth heat pump'. *ASHVE Trans.* **59**, 371–94.

[19] Sumner, J.A. (1955). 'Domestic heating by the heat pump'. *J. Inst. Heating and Ventilating Engrs.* **23** (July), 129–51.

[20] Griffith, M.V. (1952). *Heat pump sources. Heat transfer from soil to buried pipes.* ERA report Y/T18, Electrical Research Association, Leatherhead, U.K.

[21] Sumner, J.A. (1948). 'The Norwich heat pump'. *Proc. Inst. Mech. Engrs.* **158**, 22–9.

[22] Montagnon, P.E. and Ruckley, A.L. (1954), 'The Festival Hall heat pump'. *J. Inst. Fuel* **127**, 170–92.

[23] Ferranti, B. de (1955). 'Heat pumps in the house'. *Electrical Times* 27 October, 627–8.

[24] Anon. (1958). 'All-electric housing using the heat pump'. *Heating* **20**, 192–6.

[25] Halmos, E.E. (1975). 'Defense Dept. withdraws ban'. *Air Conditioning, Heating and Refrigeration News,* 8 September, 1 and 4.

[26] Edison Electric Institute (1971). *Heat pump improvement research project final report.* EEI Publication No. 71–901, New York.

[27] Groff, G.C. (1980). 'Heat pumps in the USA: 1950–1990'. *Elektrowärme Int.* Edn A, **38**, 214–21.

[28] Field, A.A. (1977). 'Aggressive selling or painstaking groundwork?' *Building Services Engr.,* **6** (45), A21–A22.

[29] Nyberg, H. (1975). *Results obtained from Swedish State Power Board measurements on heat pumps.* (Paper presented at Heat Pumps Symposium, Stockholm, Nov. 1974), Swedish Council for Building Research Publication T2: 1975, Stockholm. (Translated as O.A. Trans. 2005, 1975, Electricity Council, London.)

[30] Bernier, J. (1975). 'Air–air heat pumps'. *Revue Pratique du Froid et du Conditionnement d'Air* **28** (378), 69–83. (Translated as O.A. Trans. 2004, 1975, Electricity Council, London.)

[31] Shepherd, L. (1973). 'Review of integrated buildings in Great Britain'. *Electrowärme Int.* **31** (A1), A33–37.

[32] Hadenfeldt, A. (1976). 'Berriebserfahrungen mit der Wärmerückgewinnung in einem Hamburger Lenensmittel-Supermakt'. (Operating experience with heat recovery in a Hamburg supermarket). *Elektrowärme Int.* **34** (A5), A223–A229. Also many other articles in same journal.

[33] Building Research Establishment (1975). *Energy conservation: a study of energy consumption in buildings and possible means of saving energy in housing.* CP56/75, B.R.E., Watford, UK.

[34] Bubenko, J.A. and Fikri, Z. (1975). *Heat pump applications in Sweden – Research and Development Needs.* Royal Insititute of Technology, Stockholm.

[35] Heap, R.D. (1977). 'American heat pumps in British houses'. *Elektrowärme Int.* **35** (A2), A77–A81.

[36] Blundell, C.J. (1977) 'Optimising heat exchangers for air-to-air space heating heat pumps in the U.K.'. *Int. J. Energy Res.* **1**, 69–94.

[37] Sarkes, L.A., Nicholls, J.A. and Menzer, M.S. (1977). 'Gas fired heat pumps: an emerging technology'. *ASHRAE J.* **19** (3), 36–41.

[38] Stal Levin Ltd., Trade Literature and press releases, West Drayton, UK.

[39] Gfeller, R. (1982). 'The possibilities of waste-heat recovery by heat pumps, shown on the basis of several studies and plants realised in Switzerland'. In

*International Symposium on the Industrial Application of Heat Pumps,* Coventry, UK. BHRA Fluid Engineering, Cranfield, UK, pp. 141–160.

[40] Hodgett, D.L. and Oelert, G. (1982). 'IEA common study on advanced heat pump systems, technology survey. Part 1: Research and Development trends, Part 2: Assessment of systems and conclusions.' *Int. J. Refrig.* **5** (3), 160–8 and 169–75.

[41] Gordian Associates, Inc. (1978). *Heat pump technology: A survey of technical developments, market prospects and research needs.* US Department of Energy, Washington DC.

[42] Andrews, J.W. (1980). *Solar assisted heat pump research and development programme in the US.* BNL-27722, Brookhaven National Laboratory, Upton, New York.

[43] Spielvogel, L.G. (1980). 'The solar bottom line'. *ASHRAE J.* **22** (11), 38–40.

[44] Kirschbaum, H.S. and Veyo, S.E. (1977). *Investigation of methods to improve heat pump performance and reliability in a northern climate.* Final report, Vols. 1, 2, and 3, Westinghouse Electric Corp., Pittsburgh, Pa.

[45] Zegers, P. (ed.) (1981). *New ways to save energy. The community's energy R & D programme energy conservation.* EUR 7389 EN, Commission of the European Communities Brussels.

[46] Zegers, P. and Knobbout, J. (1982). 'An overview of the work on industrial and domestic heat pumps in the energy R&D programme of the European Community'. In *International Symposium on the Industrial Application of Heat Pumps,* Coventry UK. BHRA Fluid Engineering, Cranfield, UK, pp. 243–50.

[47] Strub, A.S. and Ehringer, H. (eds) (1980). 'New ways to save energy.' *Proceedings of EEC seminar,* EEC, Brussels.

[48] Foster, J.H. (1979). *A review of heat pump research in UK universities, polytechnics and institutes of technology.* RL-79-050, Rutherford Laboratory, Didcot, UK.

[49] Energy Technology Support Unit (1979). *A register of research, development, and demonstration in the United Kingdom. Part 1: energy conservation,* ETSU, Harwell, UK.

[50] Eklund, S.A. (1979). 'Heat pump research in Sweden'. In *Heat pump and space conditioning systems for the 1990s,* Carrier Corporation, Syracuse, NY, pp. 25–36.

[51] Jacobsen, C. (1982). 'Technical and economical experience of large heat pump plants'. In *International Symposium on the Industrial Application of Heat Pumps,* Coventry, UK. BHRA Fluid Engineering, Cranfield, UK pp. 285–308.

[52] Filkov, V.M. and Yankov, V.S. (1979). *A survey of heat pump research in the USSR.* O.A. Translation 2275, Electricity Council, London.

[53] Gatchilov, T., Diakov, D. and Iltcheva, D. (1981). *Analysis of the results obtained from the Bulgarian developments with heat pump units.* Paper presented at the International Institute of Refrigeration, Commissions B1, B2, E1, E2, Essen, West Germany, September 1981.

# Theoretical principles
# and operating cycles

2

The first proposed and most straightforward heat pumping cycle involves compression and expansion of air. However, compression and expansion of a saturated vapour/liquid mixture in a vapour compression cycle is more efficient and this principle is used in most heat pumps. Chemical absorption, which is operated by heat rather than mechanical energy, is an alternative to mechanical vapour compression. Latent heat recovery in large-scale concentration and distillation processes is possible using an open heat pump cycle in which the refrigerant itself is also the material being processed.

In this chapter the theoretical principles behind these types of heat pump are outlined together with other physical and chemical phenomena which have been proposed as means of pumping heat. They include thermoelectric heat pumping, steam-jet compressors, vortex tubes and chemical heat pumps.

## 2.1 Air-cycle machines

When a fixed quantity of gas is compressed, as is air in a bicycle pump, it becomes warmer. If it is expanded, as is carbon dioxide in leaving a soda syphon bulb, it cools. For any gas the basic relationships between pressure ($P$), volume ($V$) and temperature ($T$) are described by the gas laws, the absolute temperature of the gas being proportional to the product of its pressure and its volume, $PV/T =$ a constant. These principles were used by Thomson when he first proposed the possibility of heat pumping.

If a quantity of air is drawn by a piston into a cylinder at less than atmospheric pressure, it will expand and cool. This cooled air may then be left for a while to collect heat from its surroundings. If after warming up it is compressed, it will be heated to a higher temperature than its surroundings, and the compressed, heated air will be able to provide both useful heat and motive force for drawing in further air. This is the simplest form of the open heat pump cycle, using air as the working fluid.

If appreciable amounts of heat are to be pumped, large volumes of air and large heat exchangers are required. The c.o.p. is very sensitive to loss of efficiency in expansion and compression, because the compression work and expansion work recovery are both large compared to the net work of the cycle. This means that a small change in compression or expansion efficiency has a large effect on the net work.

The performance of the open air-cycle has been assessed by Cooper and Sumner [1]. Under typical heat pump operating conditions, and using a pressure ratio of 3 in an air cycle, the ideal theoretical c.o.p. is shown to be approximately half that of a typical vapour compression cycle. At realistic compression and expansion efficiencies, this ratio falls to one-third or less. It is shown that adding moisture to the air can improve the theoretical c.o.p., but this gives no advantage at practicable compression efficiencies.

Air-cycle machines were used successfully for refrigeration on board ship in the last century, where the absence of toxic fluids outweighed the disadvantages of bulk and of poor efficiency. The principle was developed further by Lèbre, and a multi-cellular rotary machine was used to extract heat from stale ventilation air in Zurich Congress Hall in the late 1930s [2]. Modern applications have been limited to cooling devices using compressed air produced as a by-product of other processes, as in aircraft air conditioning units in which the jet engine provides the necessary compression [3]. Rovac Corporation have developed a high-speed rotary sliding-vane air compressor for air-cycle coolers for automobiles, which might be more widely applicable [4].

The cycle described above need not be limited to air, and heat pump applications using either open or closed gas cycle machines with heat exchangers and thermal regenerators have occasionally been considered [5, 6]. Such machines may offer the chance of high theoretical efficiencies, but no commercial unit has appeared to date, and development is very limited in its extent. Closed gas cycle machines working on Stirling and other cycles are well reviewed by Walker [7].

## 2.2 The vapour compression cycle

Vapour compression heat pumps operate by continuously changing the physical properties of a fluid through a cycle approximating to the theoretical reversed Carnot cycle, which is illustrated in Fig. 2.1. A vapour is isothermally expanded from A to B at an absolute temperature $T_0$ and absorbs heat, and is then adiabatically compressed and further heated to temperature $T_1$ at C. Heat is then released during isothermal compression CD, and adiabatic expansion DA returns the vapour to its starting condition. As the cycle is plotted on axes of temperature and entropy (heat

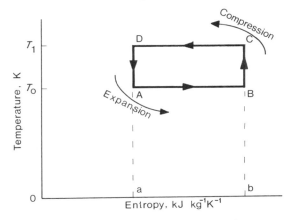

*Fig. 2.1* The reversed Carnot cycle.

energy per degree of absolute temperature), areas on the figure represent amounts of energy. Area ABCD represents the net work input, and area abCD represents the heat released, so that the heat pumping c.o.p. of this ideal theoretical cycle is $T_1/(T_1 - T_0)$, both temperatures being expressed on an absolute temperature scale (K or °R). This ratio is generally known as the heat pump 'Carnot efficiency' between $T_1$ and $T_0$.

In practical vapour compression heat pumps, the isothermal changes of state occur in a mixture of saturated vapour and liquid, and become constant pressure processes. If a suitable working fluid is used, the entropy increase during expansion is small compared to the changes during the constant pressure processes, and an efficient cycle is possible even if the expansion energy is not recovered. For practical engineering reasons dry vapour is necessary throughout the compression stage. The resultant heat pump cycle is the Rankine cycle, illustrated on both temperature/entropy and pressure/enthalpy coordinates in Fig. 2.2.

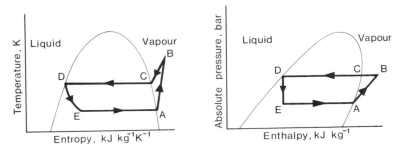

*Fig. 2.2* The vapour compression refrigeration cycle.

Vapour is compressed from point A to point B, with a temperature increase greater than in the ideal Carnot cycle, and is then cooled to point C. (The vapour at B is stated to be 'superheated' as it is above its saturation temperature for its pressure.) The vapour is condensed from C to D, expanded at constant enthalpy to E, and regains heat by evaporation from E to A. Heat is released from C to D at the condensation temperature, and a proportion of the total heat is released at a higher temperature between B and C. This heat is collected both from evaporation EA and from the work of compression between A and B. The theoretical c.o.p. is given by $(h(B) - h(D))/(h(B) - h(A))$, where $h(A)$, $h(B)$, $h(D)$ are enthalpy values at points A, B and D, respectively.

The basic components of a vapour compression heat pump are shown in Fig. 2.3, in which the refrigerant states at A, B, C, D and E correspond to those in Fig. 2.2. An orifice or tube is used as an expansion device, in place of the ideal expander machine from which work would be extracted in a reverse Carnot cycle. The properties of real refrigerant fluids, together with pressure losses in pipes and finite temperature differences in heat exchangers, make the analysis of any real cycle relatively complex, with a c.o.p. much below the theoretical Carnot and Rankine cycle values. Examples showing the methods of analysis of actual refrigeration cycles are given in standard thermodynamics textbooks. Such analyses are independent of the type of compressor or motor used. Comparisons of theoretical and actual c.o.p. have been made by Ambrose [8] for small unitary heat pumps with electric motor drives, showing an overall c.o.p. of about 13% of the ideal Carnot values. A practical example will now be given, in which it is seen that most of the drop from the ideal efficiency is due to the need to use reasonably sized heat exchangers.

Consider an air-to-air heat pump which is designed to maintain a room at

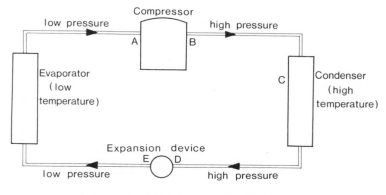

*Fig. 2.3* A basic vapour compression heat pump.

20°C when the outdoor temperature is at a typical British winter temperature of 5°C. The maximum theoretical c.o.p. is 293 K/(293 K − 278 K) = 19.5. In order to transfer heat from the outdoor air to the heat exchanger and in turn to the refrigerant using reasonable sized heat exchangers, a refrigerant evaporating temperature of − 5°C in the outdoor coil is needed, and a condensing temperature of 45°C is required to supply warm air from the indoor coil. Between these temperatures the ideal Carnot c.o.p. is 6.4. The use of non-reversible expansion (i.e. a Rankine cycle) reduces this figure to 5.1 using refrigerant 22, still under idealized conditions. As conditions can never be ideal, the c.o.p. is reduced further by compression inefficiencies to 4.0, and to 3.3 by the effect of fan power needed to blow air over the heat exchanger surfaces (taken as 5% of the total output). Pressure drops in refrigerant piping, energy use by control circuits, and the energy requirement for removing frost formed on the outdoor heat exchanger give a final reduction to a c.o.p. of 3.0, which can be obtained by careful design with real equipment. Clearly there is scope for many of the various 'inefficiencies' to be larger, and a lower figure is achieved by the majority of readily available, mass-produced units. This example illustrates that, in small machines at least, attention to optimal choice of heat exchangers and fans or pumps is likely to be the best way of ensuring an efficient design.

In larger systems more complex vapour compression cycles may warrant attention and in specialist systems, having to work across very large temperature differences, more efficient cycles with a number of successive compression stages may be essential. A two-stage system is illustrated in Fig. 2.4, in which there are two compression stages, two expansion valves, and an intermediate pressure flash chamber in which vapour which would otherwise serve no useful purpose at the evaporator is extracted and

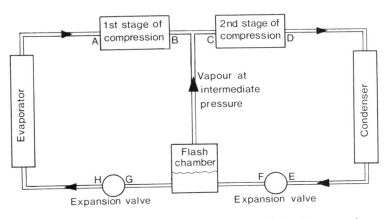

*Fig. 2.4* Two-stage vapour compression system with double expansion.

recompressed. This cycle is shown on a pressure/entropy diagram in Fig. 2.5, the lettered points corresponding to the stage of the refrigerant at the corresponding points in Fig. 2.4. By comparison with a single-stage cycle between the same pressures (the dotted lines in Fig. 2.5) there are reductions in both sub-cooling (cooling of the liquid refrigerant below the saturation temperature) and superheating, leading to an increase in overall efficiency.

An example of the improved efficiency of this two-stage cycle is shown in Fig. 2.6 based on calculations by Duminil [9]. Optimum performance depends on the correct choice of interstage pressure which is generally considered to be the geometric mean of the extreme pressures. Detailed analysis shows this to be an over-simplification and the true optimum for R12 refrigerant has been shown to be at a higher value than this [10, 11]. Although single-stage machines can pump across temperature differences of up to about 80 K with a useful c.o.p., multiple-stage cycles should be considered for temperature differences in this region and above. For smaller temperature differences the performance advantages of machines using multi-stage cycles are generally outweighed by the lower costs of single-stage units. The use of heat pumps in series ('cascade' cycles) will allow heat pumping over very wide temperature differences, and is commonly applied to the liquefaction of gases and in a number of applications in the dairy industry. The detailed analysis of various complex cycles is described by Duminil and applications of such cycles to low temperature applications and to applications requiring multiple heat exchangers are discussed further in [12].

An analysis of the practical performance of a range of such systems for possible industrial application has been carried out by Perry, showing clearly

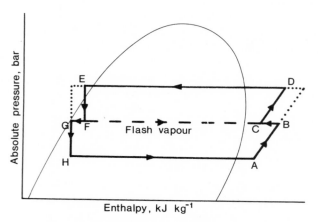

*Fig. 2.5* Two-stage vapour compression cycle.

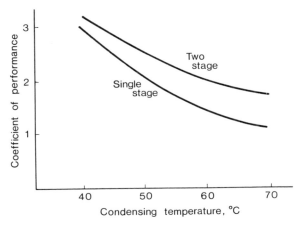

*Fig. 2.6* Comparison of single- and two-stage heat pump performance. Theoretical estimates of practical performance based on analysis by Duminil for R12 refrigerant, 20°C evaporation temperature, 45°C vapour to compressor.

that highest efficiency does not necessarily correspond to lowest operating cost [13]. An example of a cascade system is given in Chapter 7, where an R22 low-temperature cycle providing condenser heat to the evaporator of an R114 high-temperature cycle provides a temperature difference of 102 K with a c.o.p. of approximately 2.0.

As an alternative to the use of multi-stage cycles to improve efficiency it is possible to modify the conventional single-stage cycle. One proposal [14] is for a regenerative cycle in which vapour collected in an accumulator placed before the evaporator is fed occasionally to the compressor to effectively pre-cool the liquid fed to the evaporator. This increases cooling capacity whilst using only one compression stage and one expansion device, but puts additional strains on the compressor protection and other control systems. Developments of this sort, perhaps in combination with hot gas defrost systems, could be features of smaller heat pumps in the future.

## 2.3 Absorption cycles

The use of absorption cycles in refrigeration is well established, both for very small units running with no mechanical parts and for very large units using industrial waste heat. Absorption cycles are appreciably less efficient than vapour compression cycles so their use in intermediate sizes has been limited. The basic components of an absorption-cycle heat pump are shown in Fig. 2.7. The condenser, evaporator, and main expansion device are all as in a vapour compression unit, but the compressor is replaced by an absorber, a generator, and a small pump. Refrigerant is absorbed into a fluid absorbent which is cooled externally in order to increase its absorption capacity. The concentrated solution of refrigerant in absorbent is pumped to the heated generator where refrigerant vapour is driven off at an increased pressure, and the depleted absorbent is returned to the absorber. Commonly used refrigerant/absorbent pairs are ammonia/water and water/lithium bromide.

The motive power for the cycle is the heat supplied to the generator, and only a proportion of this may be usefully extracted. Heat removed from the absorber may be at too low a temperature to be useful. By considering the absorber/generator loop as a Carnot cycle heat engine driving a reverse Carnot cycle heat pump, the ideal thermodynamic limit to the c.o.p. of a single-stage absorption heat pump may be calculated as

$$\frac{T_c}{T_c - T_e} \left\{ 1 - \frac{T_e T_a}{T_c T_g} \right\}$$

where $T_e$, $T_c$ are evaporation and condensation temperatures, and $T_a$, $T_g$ are absorber and generator temperatures, all on an absolute temperature scale. This differs from the ideal c.o.p. of a vapour compression heat pump by the term in brackets, which must always be less than one. At evaporating temperatures between $-10°C$ and $+10°C$, 25% to 40% of the c.o.p. of a vapour compression unit is feasible, but if the generator heat is produced cheaply either in money or energy terms, the system can be competitive.

The basic theoretical absorber/generator cycle is shown in Fig. 2.8, for an ammonia/water system operating between a concentrated solution con-

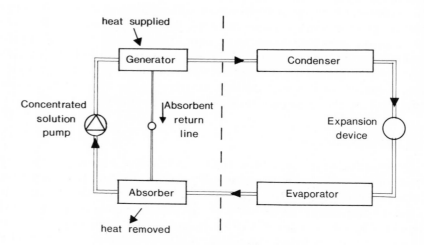

*Fig. 2.7* Absorption cycle heat pump.

taining 60% ammonia and a dilute solution with 10% ammonia. Practical cycles are more complex, frequently including a number of intermediate heat exchangers to increase overall efficiency. The refrigerant-rich liquid from the pump may be pre-heated by the refrigerant vapour leaving the generator, and then heated further by the absorbent returning to the absorber. This provides partial recovery of the heat applied to the generator.

One advantage of the absorption cycle is that it can use a relatively low-temperature heat input to produce a cooling effect. In a reversible heat pump this can be used to advantage to provide some summer cooling from solar heat. However, as a heating-only unit, a steady running c.o.p. of 1.2 to 1.4 is the highest feasible from a simple practical system. It has been demonstrated that the effects of intermittent operation can reduce this figure drastically [15], and the development of a unit showing a worthwhile seasonal c.o.p. for space heating is still awaited. Research is in progress in the US, Germany, Italy and Britain, mainly with directly fired gas units, and equipment based on absorption chillers is commercially available in Germany.

Choice of refrigerant/absorbent pair is important. Ammonia/water is most frequently used but the combination of the high operating pressure in the system, toxicity, and low c.o.p. means there is little scope for the design of a worthwhile unit unless waste heat is utilized for the generator [16].

The water/lithium bromide combination, although not suitable for low evaporator temperatures at which the water would freeze, has been recommended for pumping from sources at 60–80°C. Under these conditions a c.o.p. of 1.3 is claimed [17].

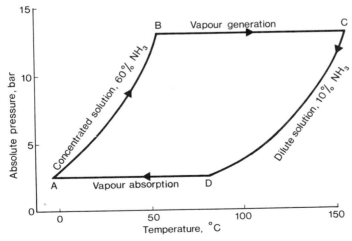

*Fig. 2.8* The basic ammonia/water absorption cycle.

The combination of R22 and E181 (dimethylether of tetraethylene glycol) is being evaluated in a number of research projects, one of which has demonstrated a c.o.p. of 1.2 when pumping from 0°C to 45°C [18, 19]. At lower temperatures, R21/DMF (dimethylformamide) has been proposed [20]. The search for new operating mixtures continues and many combinations have been considered including solid absorbents [21, 22, 23]. No ideal pair has yet been identified [24], but with existing pairs if waste heat is available to the generator there can be worthwhile applications as long as there is a demand for all the heat supplied. Capital costs of absorption systems can be high, so they are only likely to be attractive in applications in which they will run for a large proportion of their lifetime.

## 2.4 Thermoelectric heat pumps

In 1834, Peltier discovered that when a direct electric current passes round a circuit incorporating two different metals, one contact area is heated and the other cooled, which is which depending on the direction of current flow. This effect, the Peltier effect, provides a means for pumping heat without using moving parts. In a circuit containing two junctions between dissimilar conductors, heat may be transferred from one junction to the other by applying a d.c. voltage (Fig. 2.9).

To be effective, the conductors must provide high thermoelectric power and low thermal conductivity combined with adequate electrical conductivity. Such a combination of properties is not to be found in metallic conductors, and this principle could not be applied to heat pumping until the advent of semi-conductor materials, typically bismuth, antimony, selenium, and tellurium alloys. The effectiveness of materials for such applications is measured by the 'figure of merit', $Z$, defined by $Z = a^2/k\rho$, where $a$ is the Seebeck coefficient, $k$ is the thermal conductivity, and $\rho$ is the electrical resistivity of the material. Using presently available materials for which $Z =$

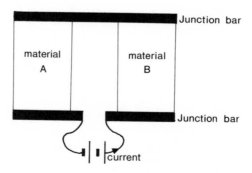

*Fig. 2.9* Peltier module.

$0.003 \text{ K}^{-1}$, thermoelectric heat pump performances about half as good as those of typical vapour compression machines can be predicted. Practical devices only achieve half these predicted values.

The limitations of known materials and the scope for possible future developments of new materials have been considered by Farrell [25]. If semi-conductors were to be developed with $Z = 0.006 \text{ K}^{-1}$ or greater there could be a considerable widening of thermoelectric heat-pumping applications and a c.o.p. comparable with those obtainable with vapour compression machines might be achieved. In applications in which vapour compression equipment can be used it is invariably both cheaper and more efficient. Thermoelectrical devices will not be competitive with vapour compression heat pumps in the foreseeable future, but they may find increasing use in specialized cooling applications where power requirements are low or where silent operation is necessary. Close temperature control of electronic components and cold stores in nuclear submarines are examples of these.

To operate semi-conductor Peltier cells, a high direct current at a low voltage is required and consequently a large number of cells are connected together in series. Heat exchangers are also required at hot and/or cold junctions to transfer heat as needed. Attempts have been made to construct practical devices for space heating and cooling. Tests of such devices in Germany have been reported [26] and units have been advertised for sale but high costs, relatively low efficiency, and dubious reliability have prevented their general use. The biggest practical problem is the electrical connection of a large number of low-voltage modules in such a way as to be reliable without producing appreciable heat conduction. From time to time manufacturers have produced prototypes and as recently as 1980 a French company was hoping to enter the market.

## 2.5 Other heat pump types

The open-cycle, vapour recompression evaporator provides a very efficient means of concentrating dilute solutions using the solvent removed as the operating fluid. The latent heat of vaporization is recovered when the evaporated vapour is condensed following compression and the excess solvent is then available for recovery if required. Alternatively, the process may be used to obtain a purer solvent, as for example in desalination of sea water. Applications of mechanical vapour recompression (as it is generally known) are discussed in Section 7.3.

The ejection of gas from a nozzle into an expander can be used to increase the pressure in a secondary circuit in which the same gas is used as a refrigerant. This method has been applied using steam as the working fluid, primarily to obtain cooling using a conventional steam boiler, but the efficiency of all such systems is low. Calculations and experiments with such systems using refrigerant R11 show clearly that theoretical c.o.p.s of less than 0.5 are possible, but that real systems yield only half this value [27]. Heat pumping applications may exist where there is spare steam, possibly in large-scale total energy schemes.

A number of other methods of heat pumping have been proposed which have not, to date, been tested in practical devices. These include vortex tubes and so-called 'chemical' heat pumps. The vortex tube heat pump makes use of an effect known as the Ranque effect. If a high pressure gas is injected tangentially into a tube, a vortex is formed and the gas at the centre of the tube is at a lower temperature and pressure than the gas near the tube wall. The gas can be extracted separately from these two regions, yielding heated or cooled gas as required. Although in principle air can be used to provide heat by this means, a sufficiently efficient device to be worth developing has never been demonstrated.

Chemical heat-pump systems have been proposed based on the mixing and dissolution of two components. Thermodynamic analysis and consideration of material properties have been carried out theoretically, but no practical machine has emerged, the most common problem being irreversibility [28].

One chemical system could operate with water and sulphuric acid in a cycle in which low-temperature heat drives water vapour to an acid absorption vessel from which high-temperature heat is released. This is a charge/discharge cycle rather than a continuously operating system and is really more a heat store than a heat pump. A sorption and desorption system for hydrogen on and from lanthanum pentanickel has been proposed [29]. A magnetic system using gadolinium, which has a Curie point at low temperature, has also been proposed. Turning an electromagnet on and off produces alternate heating and cooling in this rare earth metal. Such systems are unlikely to be used other than in extremely specialized applications.

## References

[1] Cooper, K. W. and Sumner, L. E. (1978). 'An open air cycle study using moist air thermodynamics'. *ASHRAE J.* **20** (1), 68–71.
[2] Onslow, D. V. (1945). *The heat pump for space heating.* Technical Report Y/T7, BEAIRA, London.
[3] Rogers, G. F. C. and Mayhew, Y. R. (1969). *Engineering thermodynamics, work, and heat transfer.* Longmans, Green, London.
[4] Lindsley, E. F. (1973). 'Air conditioning without a refrigerant'. *Popular Science* August, 60–1.
[5] Kennedy, D. (1973). 'The potential of the heat actuated heat pump'. *American Gas Association Monthly* **55** (April), 18–21, 25.
[6] Didion, D., Maxwell, B. and Ward, D. (1977). *A laboratory investigation of a Stirling engine driven heat pump.* (Paper presented at UNESCO International Seminar, Heat and Mass Transfer in Buildings, Dubrovnik, Yugoslavia, August/September 1977.)

[7] Walker, G. (1980). *Stirling Engines*. Oxford University Press, Oxford, UK.
[8] Ambrose, E. R. (1974). 'The heat pump: performance factor, possible improvements'. *Heating, Piping and Air Conditioning* May, 77–82.
[9] Duminil, M. (1976). 'Basic principles of thermodynamics as applied to heat pumps'. pp. 97–154 in: Camatini, E. and Kester, T. (1976). *Heat pumps and their contribution to energy conservation*. Noordhoff, Leyden, Netherlands.
[10] Fornasieri, E., Strada, M. and Zecchin, R. (1977). *Optimum design of multistage refrigeration cycles*. Paper presented at International Institute of Refrigeration, Commissions B1, B2, E1, Belgrade, November 1977.
[11] Prasad, M. (1981). 'Optimum interstage pressure for 2-stage refrigeration systems'. *ASHRAE J.* **23** (1), 58–60.
[12] *ASHRAE handbook of fundamentals* (see bibliography).
[13] Perry, E. J. (1981). *Drying by cascaded heat pumps*. Paper presented to Institute of Refrigeration, London.
[14] Granryd, E. G. U. (1975). *A regenerative refrigeration cycle*. (Paper presented at XIV International Congress of Refrigeration, Moscow.) Royal Institute of Technology, Stockholm.
[15] Lazzarin, R. (1980). 'Steady and transient behaviour of LiBr absorption chillers of low capacity'. *Int. J. Refrig.* **3** (4), 213–8.
[16] Baehr, H. D. (1981). 'The COP of absorption and resorption heat pumps with ammonia-water as working fluid'. *Int. J. Refrig.* **4** (2), 83–6.
[17] Salazar, A., Prevost, M. and Bugarel, R. (1981). 'Economie d'energie: pompe à chaleur à absorption' (Energy saving: absorption heat pump). *Int. J. Refrig.* **4** (3), 126–30.
[18] Zegers, P. (ed.) (1981). *New ways to save energy. The Community's energy R&D programme energy conservation*, EUR 7389 EN, Commission of the European Communities, Brussels.
[19] Janssen, H. A. and Oelert, G. (1978). 'Development of a primary energy driven absorption heat pump for domestic heating'. *Proceedings of meeting on Industrial Processes Energy Conservation R&D*, EUR 6326, 193–204.
[20] Badarinarayana, K., Srinivasa Murthy, S. and Krishna Murthy, M. V. (1982). 'Thermodynamic analysis of R21-DMF vapour absorption refrigeration systems for solar energy applications'. *Int. J. Refrig.* **5** (2), 115–19.
[21] Ellington, R. T., Kunst, G., Peck, R. E., and Reed, J. F. (1957). *The absorption cooling process*. Research Bulletin No. 14, Institute of Gas Technology, Chicago, Illinois.
[22] Worsøe-Schmidt, P. (1977). *A solar-powered solid-absorption refrigeration system*. Paper presented at International Institute of Refrigeration, Commissions B1, B2, E1, Belgrade, November 1977.
[23] Iedema, P.D. (1981). *A new mixture for the absorption heat pump: LiBr/ZnBr₂/ CH₃OH*. Paper presented at the International Institute of Refrigeration, Commissions B1, B2, E1, E2, Essen, West Germany, September 1981.
[24] Hodgett, D. L. and Oeleret, G. (1982). 'IEA common study on advanced heat pumps systems, technology survey. Part 1: Research and Development trends. Part 2: Assessment of systems and conclusions.' *Int. J. Refrig.* **5** (3), 160–8 and 169–75.
[25] Farrell, T. (1975), *Thermoelectric heat pumping*, ECRC/R844, Electricity Council Research Centre, Chester, UK.
[26] Spanke, D. (1968). 'Air conditioning using heat pumps and Peltier cells', *Elektrowärme Int.* **26** (6), 220–7. (Translated as O.A. Trans. 1152, 1971, Electricity Council, London.)

[27] Hamner, R. M. (1980). 'An alternate source of cooling: the ejector-compression heat pump'. *ASHRAE J.* **22** (7), 62–6.
[28] Zito, R. (1963). 'Heat pump utilizing the latent heat of dissolution'. *ASHRAE J.* **5** (7), 24–34.
[29] Wolf, S. (1975). 'Hydrogen sponge heat pump'. pp. 1348–51. in: *10th Intersoc. Energy Convers. Eng. Conf. Record.* University of Delaware, Newark.

# Vapour compression heat pumps

# 3

Vapour compression machines operating on a Rankine cycle are established as the most suitable machines for general refrigeration and heat pumping duties. They combine efficiency with compactness and safety at a reasonable cost, and are unlikely to be displaced by other equipment in the foreseeable future.

Many of the components of these machines are substantially the same whether they are used for refrigeration or heat pumping, but the additional importance of minimizing energy use in heat pumps means that some components, notably heat exchangers and fans, will be sized according to different criteria. Control systems may be more complex in heat pump installations.

The choice of components (with respect to both price and performance) depends on the particular application. Although the design considerations relating to each individual component are relatively straightforward, experience is needed in knowing the likely interactions, and wherever possible the design of a vapour-compression heat pump should be left to an engineer experienced in refrigeration equipment practices.

The sections which follow summarize the requirements of various components of the heat pump, providing both a checklist for the designer and an insight into the possible scope for design variations for the specifier. A possible refrigerant circuit for a reversible air-to-air heat pump is shown in Fig. 3.1, illustrating how the various components may be interconnected.

## 3.1 Refrigerants

The refrigerant is the life blood of the vapour compression cycle. Heat is collected and released by changes of state of the refrigerant, and is moved by its circulation. The suitability of a substance as a refrigerant depends first on the relationship between its boiling point, temperature, and pressure being such as to ensure that heat can be transferred within a practicable pressure

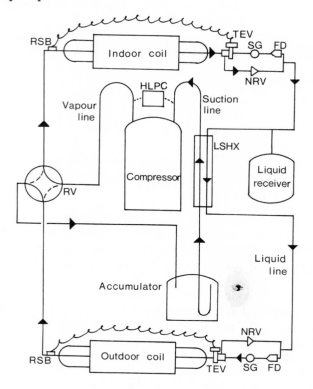

*Fig. 3.1* A possible circuit for a reversible air-to-air heat pump (arrows indicate flow
path for heating application).

Key:

| | |
|---|---|
| TEV | thermostatic expansion valve (refrigerant flow controller) |
| RSB | remote sensing bulb |
| SG | sight glass |
| FD | filter dryer |
| NRV | non-return valve |
| HLPC | high and low pressure cut-outs |
| LSHX | liquid/suction heat exchanger |

range, and secondly on its having a large enough latent heat to be able to
pump energy efficiently. The properties of a refrigerant may be conveniently plotted on a Mollier diagram, the essentials of which are shown in Fig.
3.2. Such diagrams, in addition to tabulated data, may be obtained from
manufacturers of standard refrigerants or from reference handbooks.

Adequate heat pumping capacity depends on the refrigerant having

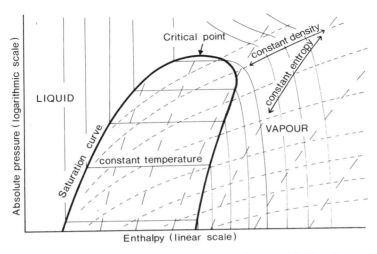

*Fig. 3.2* Representation of refrigerant properties on a Mollier diagram.

sufficient latent heat in both evaporation and condensation. This can be determined from the shape of the saturation curve and the distance of the operating pressures below the critical point (that point above which a separate liquid phase cannot exist). It is also affected by the relative slopes of the saturation curve and the isentropes (constant entropy curves), as this determines the lower limit to compressor power required for given evaporation and condensation temperatures.

Halocarbon refrigerants were first proposed in 1930 [1] and were in production and use by the early 1940s. They largely superseded ammonia, sulphur dioxide and methyl chloride in smaller applications, being less toxic and generally more suitable. Ammonia is still used in larger industrial applications such as the provision of chilled water in food processing industries, where its advantages of low cost, low volumetric displacement, and high efficiency outweigh the difficulties of handling a toxic and flammable fluid.

Refrigerants are generally known by number as refrigerant 12, refrigerant 22, etc, the number being derived from the chemical formula by taking as the first digit one less than the number of carbon atoms, as the second digit one more than the number of hydrogen atoms, and as the third digit the number of fluorine atoms (if the first digit is zero it is omitted). Thus, for example, $CClF_2CF_3$ becomes refrigerant number $(2 - 1) (0 + 1) (5) = 115$. Frequently, refrigerants are referred to by trade names ('Freon', 'Carrene', 'Arcton') or by the letter R (for refrigerant) or F (for fluorocarbon or for 'Freon'), followed by the number. Numbers 500 to 504 are reserved for azeotropic mixtures of refrigerants, which have been increasingly used since the late 1950s (particularly R500), and the 700s are used for inorganic compounds by adding 700 to their molecular weight.

Although data are readily available for perhaps 40 different possible refrigerants, there are only a few which are both readily available and suitable for general heat pump applications.

Less readily available refrigerants have been considered [2], but the established refrigerants are well proved and effective. Some of their properties are listed in Table 3.1. The values of critical temperature and latent heat of R502 are lower than those presented in several other sources. Estimated values have been widely circulated but these have subsequently been improved upon by experimental methods [3].

*Table 3.1* Properties of some refrigerants

| Refriger- ant number | Formula | Mole- cular weight | Boiling point (°C) | Critical tempe- rature (°C) | Latent heat at boiling point | |
|---|---|---|---|---|---|---|
| | | | | | kJkg$^{-1}$ | kJ mol$^{-1}$ |
| 11 | CCl$_3$F | 137.4 | 23.8 | 198.0 | 182.0 | 25.0 |
| 12 | CCl$_2$F$_2$ | 120.9 | −29.8 | 112.0 | 165.1 | 20.0 |
| 22 | CHClF$_2$ | 86.5 | −40.8 | 96.0 | 234.0 | 20.2 |
| 113 | CCl$_2$FCClF$_2$ | 187.4 | 47.6 | 214.1 | 146.7 | 27.5 |
| 114 | CClF$_2$CClF$_2$ | 170.9 | 3.6 | 145.7 | 137.2 | 23.4 |
| 500 | (R12+R152a) | 99.3 | −33.5 | 105.0 | 205.8 | 20.4 |
| 502 | (R22+R115) | 111.6 | −45.4 | 82.2 | 172.5 | 19.3 |
| 718 | H$_2$O | 18.0 | 100 | 374.2 | 2257 | 40.6 |

### 3.1.1 *Choice of refrigerant*

The basic requirements for a successful refrigerant are that it should have a high enough latent heat over the range of required condensing and evaporating temperatures for it to combine a high theoretical c.o.p. with a low mass flow rate, and that it should be physically and chemically compatible with all the other components of the equipment. In practice, the choice may be limited to those refrigerant and compressor combinations for which compressor performance data are available. The cost of the refrigerant fluid is generally low enough for this to be a secondary consideration.

The combination of Avogadro's law (that for all ideal gases the volume of 1 mol of gas is constant) and Trouton's rule (that latent heat per mol approximates to a constant multiple of the absolute temperature of the phase change) means that for a given compressor, and for given condensation and evaporation temperatures, there will not be wide variations in heat pumping capacity between different refrigerants. Such variations as there are will generally be associated with differences in operating pressure, higher capacity being obtained from higher-pressure refrigerants. The main practical factors to consider are chemical stability, toxicity, and availability.

When considering a refrigerant's chemical stability and compatibility with other materials such as piping, heat exchanger materials, valve seatings and seals, the vapour superheat (the temperature difference between the heated vapour phase and the liquid boiling point) is particularly important as these problems are most apparent at the maximum operating temperature in the cycle. Hermetic compressors often have motors which are cooled directly by refrigerant vapour, and in this case the vapour must have adequate electrical strength in addition to being compatible with the electrical insulation materials used. Many compressors are lubricated by oil circulating in contact with refrigerant, so that not only compatibility of refrigerant and oil but also miscibility must be considered, as the amount of oil carried with the refrigerant can affect heat transfer performance as well as lubrication. Corrosive contaminants such as hydrofluoric acid may be produced if halocarbon refrigerants come into contact with moisture, and to reduce the risk of this in the event of pipework leaks, it is preferable to choose a refrigerant which may be operated at above atmospheric pressure, thus preventing moist air entering the system.

Naturally, the better established air-conditioning and refrigeration system refrigerants are the most generally available and economic, and their compatibility properties are well known. This being the case, they must be first choices for any heat pump application and for space-heating heat pumps using ambient temperature heat sources, refrigerants 12, 22 and 502 have suitable physical properties. R12 is primarily used for refrigeration applications, covering a range of evaporating temperatures from $-35$ to $+10°C$, and requiring a larger compressor displacement for a given capacity than either R22 or R502. R22 has been used successfully for years in air source heat pumps but suffers from high superheat temperatures and also operates at a higher pressure than R12. Chemically, R22 is relatively insoluble in lubricating oils making oil return more difficult (though this is less of a problem with modern synthetic oils) but it is less reactive with lubricating oil, consequently maintaining oil life. It has the disadvantage of being a more destructive solvent for wire enamel, varnish, and elastomeric seals.

R502 overcomes some of the deficiencies of R22, but is more expensive, requires larger pipework due to appreciably increased pumping rates, and there is less experience with its use. The theoretical performances of these three refrigerants calculated for a condensing temperature of 40°C, and evaporating temperatures of both 0°C and −20°C are shown in Table 3.2, assuming 5K of superheat, 8K of sub-cooling, a compressor adiabatic efficiency of 60%, and a motor efficiency of 80%. Direct comparative testing of R22 and R502 in particular applications could lead to an increased use of the latter, its main advantage being increased reliability due to reduced superheat temperatures [4].

The choice of refrigerant for heat pumps operating at temperatures in excess of 90°C has been the subject of considerable recent study [5–10]. For condensing temperatures up to 120°C, R114 may be used, but pressure levels, stability in the presence of lubricating oil and a relatively high solubility in most oils prevent its use at higher temperatures. Other refrigerants studied include R12B1 ($CBrClF_2$), R133a ($CF_3CH_2Cl$), R142b ($C_2H_3ClF_2$) and for closed systems operating above 130°C, $H_2O$.

Recent studies suggest R11 and R114 are both more generally suitable than R12B1 and that if more readily available R133a could be a competitor for R114 in higher temperature ranges. The choice of refrigerant cannot be divorced from lubrication requirements, and synthetic hydrocarbon lubricants have been studied for heat-pump use by Mobil and by EdF with favourable results. Considerable work on refrigerant/lubricant combinations for higher temperatures has taken place at ECRC.

A different class of refrigerants known as Fluorinols and Flutecs consist respectively of mixtures of trifluoroethanol and water and of perfluoro-alkanes. F85 is a Fluorinol with 15% (mole) water and it has been recommended for use in the 120–180°C temperature range. However, there is no ideal fluid for these temperatures and research and evaluation continue. The range of worthwhile applications for heat pumps operating at such high temperatures is restricted to areas where high-temperature heat is essential and there is an insufficient demand for lower-temperature waste heat. This is likely to be in a limited range of industrial processes.

For the future, it has been suggested that non-azeotropic mixtures of refrigerants, which give evaporation and condensation over a range of temperatures, may have advantages [11]. The thermodynamic cycle involved (the Lorenz cycle) offers a better theoretical c.o.p. than a Carnot cycle, but at the cost of larger heat exchangers, which have to have a counter-flow of refrigerant and heat carrier. Mixtures of refrigerants may also offer scope for capacity control, by means of varying the refrigerant mixture composition by preferential condensation of one component. The use of non-azeotropic mixtures was proposed by Haselden in 1957 [12], and has more recently been strongly advocated by Kruse [13] and Rojey [14]. Claimed advantages include savings in energy use of up to 50%, increased compressor capacity up to 60%, reduced pressure ratios, and continuous capacity control. Work has been carried out on mixtures of R12/114, R22/114, R21/22, R12/13 and R13B1/R152a. Thermodynamic data on the last of

*Table 3.2* Comparison of R12, R22, R502

|  | R12 | R22 | R502 |
|---|---|---|---|
| *0°C evaporating and 40°C condensing temperature* | | | |
| C.o.p. (compressor only) | 3.66 | 3.63 | 3.52 |
| Flow (m³ h⁻¹) for 1 kW | 1.29 | 0.80 | 0.79 |
| Flow (kgh⁻¹) for 1 kW | 22.6 | 16.5 | 24.8 |
| Capacity (kW) for 1 m³ h⁻¹ | 0.78 | 1.25 | 1.27 |
| Discharge temperature (°C) | 69 | 86 | 64 |
| Condensing pressure (absolute, bar) | 9.61 | 15.33 | 16.77 |
| *−20°C evaporating and 40°C condensing temperature* | | | |
| C.o.p. (compressor only) | 2.43 | 2.41 | 2.31 |
| Flow (m³ h⁻¹) for 1 kW | 2.34 | 1.42 | 1.40 |
| Flow (kg h⁻¹) for 1 kW | 21.0 | 14.9 | 22.9 |
| Capacity (kW) for 1 m³ h⁻¹ | 0.43 | 0.71 | 0.72 |
| Discharge temperature (°C) | 87 | 113 | 79 |

these is now available [15] which will make future progress more rapid, and considerable research effort is likely, but commercial exploitation before the early 1990s seems unlikely.

Although the refrigerants which have been listed in Table 3.1 are non-flammable and generally considered non-toxic [16], the possibility of some being carcinogenic and of others having a deleterious effect on the upper atmosphere has been raised [17–19]. It has been suggested that halocarbons (particularly R11, R12, R500) reaching the stratosphere could act as catalysts for ozone depletion, which could lead to increased ultraviolet radiation reaching the earth's surface, possibly resulting in a small increase in skin cancer. Counter arguments dispute both the mechanism and the significance of any possible effect, especially as variations in the ozone layer caused by other factors such as solar activity appear to be considerable [20–23]. Halocarbon refrigerants were originally introduced partly to eliminate major toxic hazards of existing refrigerants and, as in nearly all technological developments, the reduction of obvious major risks has led later to proper consideration of less obvious side effects and to increased standards of safety and pollution control.

Several countries have considered controlling the manufacture and use of chlorofluorocarbons (CFCs). In the US their use as propellants in inessential aerosols was banned in April 1979 and Canada, Sweden and Norway have introduced similar restrictions. In 1979 the EEC proposed a voluntary 30% reduction (based on 1976 levels) in the use of CFCs in aerosols by the end of 1981, and this has been achieved. In 1980 the US Environmental Protection Agency froze production levels for CFCs while considering further restrictions in their use including refrigeration applications [24, 25]. This produced considerable concern in the refrigeration industry [26, 27] as it was felt that the real benefits of CFCs as refrigerants should not be outweighed by as yet unproved hazards and a ban on CFCs could result in greater hazards than those produced by the ozone effect. The costs of replacing existing refrigerants with new would be extremely high and would be difficult to justify before exhaustive testing of alternatives was complete [28].

As less than one-third of world halocarbon production is used in refrigeration, considerable reduction in the possible hazard can be effected without affecting refrigerant use. Additionally, encouragement of the use of arguably less harmful CFCs such as R22 [29] and of appropriate design and servicing procedures to reduce gas losses can minimize the hazards.

## 3.2  Compressor drives

### 3.2.1  Electric motors

At the present time, all small heat pumps and most larger heat pumps use electric motors to provide the mechanical work input required to operate the compressor. Electric motors are quiet, reliable, and efficient, as long as the motor characteristics are properly matched to the application. In larger motor sizes appropriate starting arrangements and power factor correction may be necessary. Variable speed inverter drives could both reduce start currents and provide compressor speed control [30], but are likely to be expensive. The effects of transient starting currents on supplies must be assessed for complete equipment assemblies, not just motors, as the transient currents can be affected substantially by interactions between the components [31]. Electric motor characteristics and their effects on electricity supply are considered further in Section 4.1.3.

### 3.2.2  Internal combustion engines

Fossil-fuel-fired internal combustion engines can have attractions as compressor drives if the engine waste heat in the exhaust gases and in the cooling water can be recovered and usefully exploited.

The diesel engine is well proved, durable, and efficient, and can be appropriate in large heat pump installations where good maintenance and inspection standards can keep both noise and pollution within acceptable limits. However, there could be dangers in applying diesel drives to smaller units (for example, on a domestic scale) as there is only a small range of operating conditions within which both carbon monoxide and nitrogen oxide emission levels can be kept low, and unattended or poorly maintained units would be unacceptable. Nevertheless, at least one small diesel unit for domestic use has been developed, with a 14 kW heating capacity [32].

The gas engine can be considered as an alternative to an electric drive whenever there is a need for a large heat pump with a fairly constant load. A case can be made for the higher capital costs of such units if the heat is required at a temperature of at least 30°C above that of the source, in which case the combination of heat pump and heat recovery from the engine exhaust and water jacket can be worthwhile. A gas engine driving a heat pump is shown in Fig. 3.3 which illustrates the engine and compressor of a 0.5 MW air-source heat pump heating an open-air swimming pool at Dortmund [33].

Further examples of gas-engine-driven heat pumps in industry and commerce are quoted in Chapters 6 and 7. Engines are available in sizes from 20 kW up, but the most worthwhile applications are in sizes from 500 kW up to several megawatts. It has been suggested that heat recovery applications and industrial space heating are the most promising markets for gas-engine heat pumps [34].

At the small end of the size range, Ford of Europe has a 1.6 litre natural gas engine which is being promoted for use in heat pumps and which is available in a number of heat pump packages. Such packages are much more expensive than conventional gas heaters and their long-term reliability has

*Fig. 3.3* Gas engine and compressor of Dortmund heat pump.

yet to be proved, but as they are potential mass-produced items costs could fall to an economic level for applications with long hours of use. The fluidic internal combustion engine has been proposed for heat pump application but this has yet to be proved viable [35].

### 3.2.3 *External combustion engines*

External combustion engines include both large steam turbines and less fully developed engines using Stirling or open or closed Rankine cycles. They have the advantage that almost any fuel may be used and they promise greater scope for waste heat recovery and very much lower pollution levels compared with internal combustion engines. Experiments on Stirling-engine-driven heat pumps are giving encouraging results in terms of efficiency [36], as most of the waste heat is readily recovered from engine cooling water, and development of equipment specifically designed for heat pump applications is well advanced.

The best known Stirling-engine-driven heat pump is that using an engine developed by Philips and installed in a pair of experimental houses near Eindhoven in Holland. A gas-fired unit with engine waste heat recovery provided 8–25 kW of heat over a compressor speed range of 750–3000 rpm, with a seasonal average c.o.p. around 1.4. In one system which is being developed in the US [37], a free-piston Stirling engine is directly linked to an inertia compressor to provide a compressor/drive unit for a 10 kW gas-fired heat pump, as illustrated in Fig. 3.4. The compressor operates in a conventional heat pump circuit, and the system includes heat recovery from the exhaust of the external combustor as well as from the Stirling engine

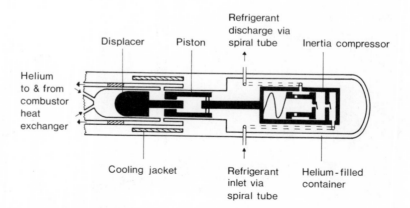

*Fig. 3.4* Inertia compressor linked to free-piston Stirling engine, after Sarkes *et al.* [37].

cooler. Prototype testing was expected to be completed in 1980, but according to Walker *et al.* in 1982, 'there appears little prospect of the impending commercial introduction of this machine' [38]. The term 'Stirling engine' covers a wide range of devices operating on closed, regenerative thermodynamic cycles, and these are fully described and discussed by Walker [39]. None have as yet demonstrated commercial viability.

A gas-fired Rankine system is detailed later in Section 5.4 (p. 128) and a prototype Rankine-cycle, vapour-driven engine has been constructed to use direct solar heat [40]. The Rankine power cycle is basically similar to the Rankine heat pump cycle run in reverse with a turbine in place of the compressor. Heat is used to evaporate and expand a fluid which drives the turbine and is then condensed and returned to the evaporator by a liquid pump. For solar powered applications a low-boiling-point fluid such as refrigerant R11 could be suitable.

An open-cycle steam turbine using steam generated by a combustion boiler may be used as a heat pump drive. This possibility is being assessed in a joint government/manufacturer project in the US [41]. If the steam turbine is directly connected to a high-speed turbine compressor a reasonably efficient system may be possible, but reliability problems with the rotating seals could arise under the severe conditions. The use of a hermetically sealed magnetic coupling between a gas turbine and a compressor has been reported [37] which could provide one answer to this problem. Sealing difficulties may also be overcome by using a closed Rankine-cycle machine for which the prime mover working fluid and the refrigerant are the same substance. Considerable development work on closed-cycle engines using organic working fluids is reported by Angelino [42], and this could have an impact on the availability of suitable fuel-fired prime movers for large-sized heat pumps in the future.

### 3.2.4 *Choice of fuel*

Availability is obviously an important factor in assessing the competitiveness of non-electric drives. For example, in remote locations where an independent source of fuel is necessary and the transport and storage costs of diesel fuel are not excessive, then a diesel-driven heat pump could well make better sense than a diesel generator supplying an electric heat pump. In applications where there is an adequate electricity supply, the case is less clear. In conventional power stations approximately one-third of the energy content of the fuel used is made available as electricity, mainly because of the thermodynamic limitations of the processes used. If this electricity is used to drive a heat pump with a c.o.p. of 3 the final heat output of the heat pump is approximately equal to the original energy content of the fuel. If an engine-driven heat pump incorporates recovery of waste engine heat, a final heat output of at least 1.3 times the fuel energy input may be possible [43]. The figures shown in Table 3.3 illustrate that 100 kW of heat may be produced from 88 kW from the gas field, by comparison with 170 kW equivalent fuel supplied to a power station. This may be used as an argument in favour of engine-driven heat pumps but it is only valid in energy terms if the power station fuel and the engine fuel are interchangeable which is seldom the case. If coal or residual oil is the power station fuel there is no energy advantage. If low-viscosity petroleum products or natural gas are used as power station fuel, then there must be a strong energy use case for fuel-fired heat pumps, but there is only likely to be any economic advantage in engine-driven heat pumps if the fuel is available more cheaply to the heat pump operator than to the generator of electricity.

The whole question of 'equivalent' fuel is a difficult one, as it involves comparing gas, which could be a chemical feedstock, with a coal equivalent, which could be crude oil residue or nuclear power or the output from a wind- or tidal-power system. In this context 'thermal equivalence' is an unnecessary concept; all the potential user is concerned with is cost in money terms. The real significance of Table 3.3 is that full use of engine waste heat recovery is necessary for the gas scheme to be worth considering. The question of overall national energy saving is very complex but any heat pump scheme is clearly preferable to using either fuel-fired or electric heating directly.

Avoiding both fossil fuel and electricity, a windmill could drive a heat pump either directly or via a hydraulic circuit, but for such a combination to be efficient the refrigerant circuit would have to be controlled so as to match

*Table 3.3* Total power requirements for 100 kW heat output [44]

| Electric motor heat pump | | | | |
|---|---|---|---|---|
| Fuel to power station | 170 kW | of which | 119 kW | 'lost' |
| To motors | 51 kW | of which | 5 kW | 'lost' |
| To fan drive | 3 kW | | | |
| To compressor drive | 43 kW | } Total output = 100 kW | | |
| Pumped from source | 57 kW | | | |
| | | | | |
| *Gas-engine heat pump* | | | | |
| From gas field | 88 kW | of which | 5 kW | 'lost' |
| To engine | 83 kW | of which { | 15 kW | 'lost'. |
| | | | 2 kW | to fan drive |
| | | | 46 kW | recovered heat |
| To compressor drive | 20 kW | } Total heat pump output 54 kW | | |
| Pumped from source | 34 kW | | | |

Heat pump output plus recovered heat = 100 kW

a very wide range of power inputs.

None of the presently available fossil-fuel-fired drives is completely adequate as a heat pump drive although there are developments in a number of directions. Whether such developments can be completed before the fuels for which the equipment is designed have become too scarce and expensive to use for this purpose is not easy to assess.

## 3.3 Compressors

The compressor both pumps refrigerant round the circuit and produces the required substantial increase in the pressure of the refrigerant. The refrigerant chosen and the operating temperature range needed for heat pumping generally lead to a need for a compressor which will provide a high pressure difference for moderate flow rates, and this is most often met by a positive displacement compressor using a reciprocating piston. Other types of positive displacement compressor use rotating vanes or cylinders or intermeshing screws to move the refrigerant. In some larger applications, centrifugal or turbine compressors are used, which are not positive displacement machines but accelerate the refrigerant vapour as it passes through the compressor housing. These various compressor types are illustrated in Fig. 3.5.

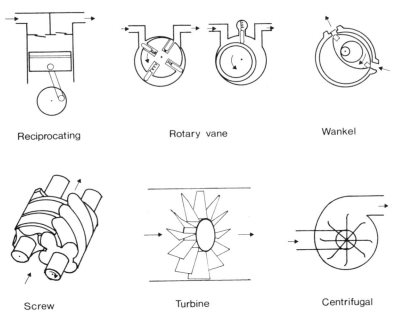

Reciprocating          Rotary vane          Wankel

Screw          Turbine          Centrifugal

*Fig. 3.5* Compressor types.

The high operating temperatures and wide range of operating conditions likely to be met in space-heating heat pumps make greater demands on compressors than do air-conditioning applications, so that purpose-designed heat pump compressors are preferable on reliability grounds to units primarily designed for the smaller range of temperatures required in air conditioning or cooling applications.

Small compressors for refrigeration use have traditionally been designed for reliability to the extent that efficiency almost becomes a secondary factor. Recent Japanese studies suggest that attention to detail with

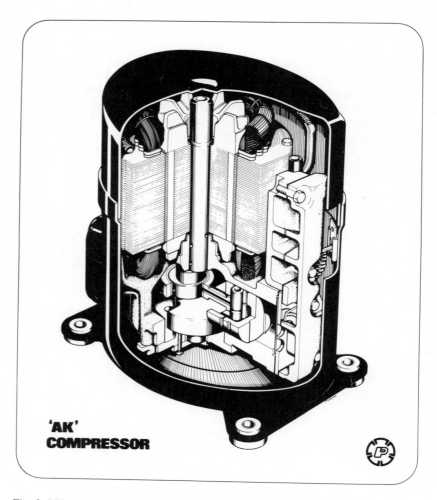

*Fig. 3.6* Hermetic motor compressor unit. Courtesy of Prestcold Holdings Ltd.

efficiency in mind can produce machinery which is up to 25% more efficient [45].

In small equipment where cost is a major factor and on-site installation is preferably kept to a minimum, hermetically sealed motor/compressor combinations, such as that illustrated in Fig. 3.6, are used. The motor is cooled by the flow of low-pressure refrigerant gas over it, and the compressor, piston and bearings are lubricated by oil which is circulated around the refrigerant circuit. This means that compatability of oil, refrigerant, and motor insulation is of fundamental importance for reliable operation. There are no rotating seals separating motor and compressor, and the internal components are not accessible for maintenance, the casing being factory welded. Overall motor plus compressor efficiencies are in the 40–60% region, varying with c.o.p. as shown in Fig. 3.7. This efficiency range covers most of the electric motor plus compressor units on the market, of all types and sizes.

A directly fired, gas-fuelled heat pump using high-speed miniature turbomachinery has been investigated. This is described in more detail in Section 5.4. The compressor in this unit is linked to a turbine drive on a common shaft, and these components are illustrated in Fig. 3.8.

In larger sizes, up to about 150 kW absorbed power, reciprocating compressors are often semi-hermetic, i.e. although motor and compressor are within one casing, this casing may be unbolted, and the refrigerant does

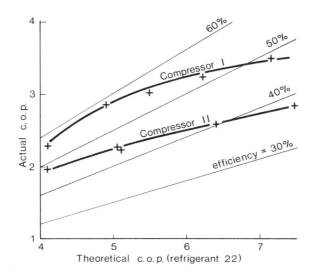

*Fig. 3.7* Efficiency of two hermetic motor/compressor units, based on manufacturers' data

*Fig. 3.8* Turbomachine rotors of a Rankine-cycle engine-driven heat pumps. Courtesy of Glynwed Group Services Ltd.

not flow over the motor windings. Access for maintenance is straightforward, but the need for external motor cooling which aids efficiency in cooling applications is no advantage in heat pump operations, and the cost is substantially higher than for hermetic units. As large motors are more efficient than small, overall efficiencies of up to 70% or more are theoretically possible [46], and in multi-cylinder compressors, capacity may be controlled by making one or more cylinders ineffective (e.g. by holding the inlet valve open). Cylinder unloading at start up is also a convenient way of reducing starting torque. 'Open' reciprocating compressors with a shaft seal and an external drive motor suitable for a range of prime movers are also available up to about 2 MW duty.

Centrifugal or turbine compressors which combine compactness with low maintenance costs are often used in place of positive displacement compressors for very large capacities, or for high-flow low-pressure difference applications, and are available, designed for refrigeration use, in the 300 kW–20 MW range. Future development of heat pumps for industrial process heat recovery could require such equipment, hermetic units being commonly used with R11, R12, or R500 for chilled-water production. Centrifugal compressors are also appropriate to multi-stage heat pump applications, where two or more compression stages may be incorporated within the same turbine housing with interstage gas injection between the rotors. For large and variable capacity applications, positive displacement screw compressors are also available in the 300–2500 kW range. These are capable of capacity variation down to 10% of rated capacity, with negligible loss of efficiency down to 30% of capacity. Smaller screw compressors using R22 are also available but dimensional tolerances to provide adequate sealing pose problems in small units. Development of efficient screw compressors of less than 100 kW capacity seems unlikely at present.

An alternative to the conventional twin-screw geometry is the Zimmern single-screw compressor in which a single cylindrical fluted rotor is meshed with freewheeling star wheels to provide compression spaces [47]. The arrangement of a commercially available unit is shown in Fig. 3.9. This geometry has been developed into commercial units over the past few years and is now available for the range 660–5000 $m^3 h^{-1}$ corresponding approximately to 0.3–6.0 MW heat pump output, depending on conditions of use. There is potential for development of smaller single-screw machines, a size of 160 $m^3 h^{-1}$ having been tested on an experimental basis [48].

The single-screw compressor offers potential advantages for high-temperature heat pump operation with R114 as refrigerant. The bearing and lubrication requirements at high temperatures are more readily met with this geometry and the presence of liquid refrigerant in the compression chambers can be tolerated. At lower temperatures R12, R22 and R502 may be used and at higher temperatures tests have been made with steam [49]. Part-load efficiency characteristics have been examined and with ammonia at a pressure ratio of 5, isentropic efficiency varied from 75% at full capacity to 50% at 30% capacity [48].

Rotary sliding vane compressors have been used in hermetic units and have advantages in robustness over reciprocating compressors. They are capable of operating as liquid pumps and therefore are able to stand considerable abuse as vapour compressors. They were mostly displaced by reciprocating units in the 1960s, but further development has been announced by at least one heat pump manufacturer and they could reappear in larger numbers in the late 1980s [50–52]. A rotary vane compressor for an air cycle unit has been described by Rovac [53].

At high flow rates, rotary piston compressors (Wankel compressors) have theoretical advantages of reliability and efficiency over both reciprocating and rotary vane units [54] and Wankel heat pump compressors are being developed. Other possible developments include oil-free reciprocating compressors [55] and very small, high-speed turbine compressors [35]. In the short term, the choice of compressor for a heat pump depends mainly on availability, but in the longer term the interdependence of prime mover, compressor, and refrigerant is such that any one of a wide range of

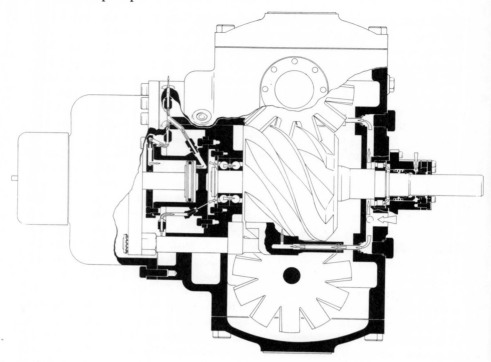

*Fig. 3.9* Arrangement of a compressor with a single screw and two star wheels. Courtesy of Hall-Thermotank Products Ltd.

combinations could prove to be the best for any particular application. However, the time scale for successful compressor development must be measured in decades, and rapid progress must not be anticipated.

### 3.3.1 *Capacity control*

Heat pumps using ambient energy sources have to work over a wide range of operating conditions. Reciprocating compressors work more efficiently at reduced speeds than they do when operating intermittently at full speed. In addition, a reduced pumping rate results in a reduced temperature difference between evaporator and condenser with a subsequent increase in system c.o.p. Consequently, the use of a variable capacity compressor (either by speed variation or by other means) makes more efficient operation at part load possible. In space-heating applications, much of the annual energy use is at less than half the peak power loading [56], and the use of even a two-speed compressor would increase seasonal efficiency appreciably. Estimates vary, but it has been suggested that continuous compressor speed control could give annual energy savings of up to 20% [46, 57].

Improvements of 9–12% (dependent on the load pattern) in seasonal efficiency have been obtained by using capacity modulation with an experimental system driven by a Stirling engine [36]. A method of using delayed suction valve opening to provide capacity control has been extensively analysed by Hiller and Glicksman [58] suggesting that in theory for reversible heat pumps up to 30% annual energy savings are possible using this technique. If compressors with capacity control were available cheaply their use could be widespread, but various authors have shown that there are at present more economic ways of improving heat pump performance, notably by increasing heat exchanger coil sizes [59– 61].

## 3.4 Heat exchangers

Heat exchangers are devices through which heat is transferred from one fluid to another without the two being mixed. For example, heat can be transferred between air and a refrigerant using a finned tube heat exchanger (Fig. 3.10), and between liquids using a shell and tube heat exchanger (Fig. 3.11). In heat pumps they are needed both to collect heat into the refrigerant circuit at the evaporator and to emit heat from it at the condenser.

The correct choice of heat exchangers and their sizing is probably the most important point in designing an efficient and economic heat pump [62]. It is also in some ways the most difficult. The complex geometries of heat exchangers, together with wide variations in operating conditions, mean that precise calculation of sizes from basic physical principles is not

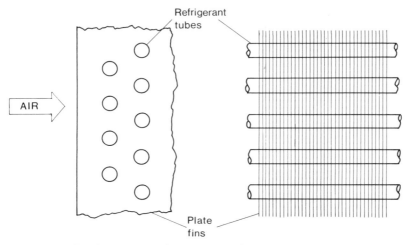

*Fig. 3.10* Fin coil (continuous fin) heater exchanger.

practicable, and various empirical factors have to be applied to heat transfer relationships which have themselves been determined by experiment. Although such factors may be well established for available heat exchanger geometries, details of them may be difficult to obtain from exchanger manufacturers anxious to maintain their competitive position.

For heat pump condensers in particular, heat transfer calculations will always be complex, as there are three distinct heat transfer regimes (refrigerant vapour cooling, condensation, and liquid subcooling) the boundaries between which vary depending on the conditions. Interactions between the condenser conditions and the operation of evaporator, compressor and controls mean that condenser optimization can only be carried out on a trial-and-error basis for assumed behaviour of other components as part of an overall system optimization (see Section 3.11).

Many aspects of heat transfer are discussed in detail in the standard texts (e.g. [63]). All simple heat transfer processes are adequately described by the basic heat transfer equation

$$q = UA\mathrm{d}T$$

where $q$ is heat flow, $U$ is a heat transfer coefficient, $A$ is the effective heat transfer area, and $\mathrm{d}T$ is the average effective temperature difference. The heat transfer coefficient $U$ is a complex function of many factors including flow rate, temperature, and properties of the materials to and from which heat is flowing. The equations for $U$, for a wide range of conditions applicable to heat pump heat exchangers, are listed in the ASHRAE handbook — *Fundamentals*. Heat transfer characteristics of a wide range of compact heat exchangers are given by Kays and London [64]. For maximum heat flow for a given value of $U$, it is obviously desirable to increase both $A$ and $\mathrm{d}T$. $A$ is frequently increased by using extended surfaces in the form of various types of fins and $\mathrm{d}T$ may be maximized by using counterflow circuits in which the fluids between which heat is being transferred flow in opposing directions over the heat exchanger.

For heat transfer between refrigerant and air or vice versa, the air is usually forcibly circulated by fans over finned coils of the type illustrated in Fig. 3.10. This is not the only possible system, and the feasibility of using natural convection, flat-plate heat exchangers for heat pump applications has been considered by Blundell [65], who found that although silent in operation they were not economic. Bernier [66] has considered a range of air-to-air and air-to-water heat pumps using natural convection and radiation evaporators and condensers. A recent system in Germany collects energy from a steel fence through which antifreeze solution is pumped for which a solar energy/ambient air heat collection of 40 $\mathrm{Wm}^{-2}$ at worst conditions is claimed [67]. Bare tube heat exchangers are sometimes used in dehumidification applications, and for some types of dehumidifier may be the optimal solution for maximum moisture removal. For relatively clean air and halocarbon refrigerants, coils formed from copper tubes with mechanically bonded aluminium fins are appropriate. Staggered tubes and wavy fins are used regularly to increase external heat transfer, and extended tube surfaces can also be used internally. Choice of coil depth, number of parallel refrigerant circuits, and fin spacing will depend on the requirements of a particular design.

For heat transfer between refrigerant and water or other liquids, heat exchangers may be either of the shell and tube variety in which the refrigerant is enclosed in a shell through which tubes containing the other liquid pass (Fig. 3.11), or of the reverse type in which refrigerant passes through tubes within another container. Although the shell and tube unit has to have a casing capable of withstanding high refrigerant pressures, the heat transfer advantages of being able to use extended tube surfaces on the refrigerant side thus increasing the effectiveness of evaporation or condensation are appreciable. A reverse system with refrigerant in the tubes is only used for very simple geometries or where there is a chance of the liquid freezing, in which case it is less liable to damage. The relative advantages of the two systems may be worth further study for heat pump applications. Other shell and tube geometries are possible in addition to the one illustrated, simple cases being the tube-in-tube geometry in which a refrigerant pipe is surrounded by a water jacket (possibly using a plastic outer tube), and the shell and coil in which a coil of refrigerant piping is immersed in a liquid storage tank. Sometimes two separate liquid flows pass through two sets of tubes within a single shell in what is known as a 'double bundle'. Some applications of double bundle condensers will be found in Chapter 6.

The choice of heat exchanger material will require particular care if it is to operate in a corrosive environment. This is readily appreciated in extreme environments, but can provide unexpected problems with impure water

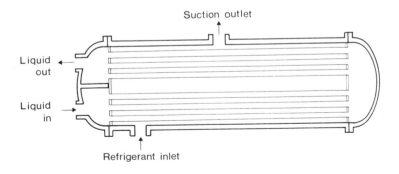

*Fig. 3.11* Shell and tube evaporator.

from natural sources, or with moist air which may contain pollutants. The use of aluminium, and particularly of aluminium alloys with a substantial magnesium content, may present a greater corrosion risk than the use of an all-copper system. On dehumidification coils, relatively small quantities of contaminant may be concentrated in the liquid collected, and the corrosion possibility must be carefully evaluated. Alternatives include all-copper, plated copper, mild or stainless steel, or plastic-coated coils. The choice will depend on the nature of both the contaminant and the application. If the refrigerant used is ammonia, steel piping must be used to avoid the corrosive reactions which take place between ammonia and copper. Steel heat exchangers are more difficult to fabricate than copper, so this is one reason why refrigerants other than ammonia are preferred.

### 3.4.1 *Design considerations*

Once the appropriate type of heat exchanger has been selected, heat exchangers must be sized to give adequate heat transfer performance. The larger the heat exchanger, the greater the heat transfer and the greater the cost. Correct sizing consists of selecting the most economic heat exchanger which will meet the performance requirements. The performance must be assessed for both the design conditions and for all other operating conditions which are likely to be met in use. (Design conditions may be specified for extreme conditions, or for the most typical operating conditions, or for both, depending on the application. If energy use is of primary importance, as is probable in heat pump applications, then the typical operating condition is the most important.) If heat exchangers are required to condense out moisture from air as well as transferring heat, the design requirements will be different from those for dry coils. This is basically because efficient heat transfer is achieved with low temperature differences, whereas efficient moisture condensation requires an appreciable temperature drop. When heat exchangers are being sized for reversible heat pumps, non-return valves are sometimes used to reduce the effective area of the indoor coil during cooling use, in order to achieve efficient dehumidification.

Heat pump evaporators, to be efficient, must operate so that the minimum amount of heat exchange surface is used for vapour superheating, 'and the maximum used for either boiling transfer or sensible transfer to liquid refrigerant. Advantages may be gained by using a subsidiary refrigerant circulation through the evaporator, maintaining it fully filled with liquid, as shown in Fig. 3.12. The design of such refrigerant recirculation systems has been considered by Lorentzen [68]. The operation of such systems requires detailed consideration of refrigerant flow control over the range of operating conditions, but the heat transfer at the exchanger is simplified.

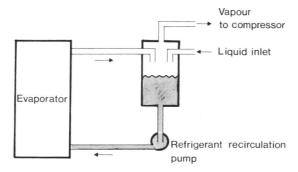

*Fig. 3.12* Refrigerant recirculation evaporator.

Refrigerant flow rates high enough to give small temperature differences and thus good heat transfer can give excessive pressure drops in single-pipe circuits. To overcome this, a number of parallel refrigerant flows are frequently arranged within one heat exchanger. Both the heat flux and the refrigerant flows must be balanced between the circuits, and to aid the flow some sort of refrigerant·distributor designed to split the flow equally for all combinations of liquid and vapour is usually necessary. If compressor lubrication oil is circulated with the refrigerant, flow rates must be compatible with adequate oil return and heat transfer performance may be altered by the presence of the oil [69, 70].

The surfaces of heat exchangers which are exposed to water, or air which may contain impurities, must be protected against excessive fouling and the design may need to allow empirically for some degree of typical fouling in service. In air coils, filters may be incorporated to reduce fouling, but fin spacing may still be limited by considerations of dust accumulation or frost formation (see Section 3.9).

The design of a heat exchanger cannot be considered in isolation. If noise is important, the combination of heat exchanger with fan or pump will have to be considered, and the combined effects of these components will also influence both capital costs and energy use. Examples of overall cost optimization of the heat exchangers and fans for air-to-air space heating heat pumps for specific countries have been published [62, 71], including detailed assessments of heat transfer characteristics.

## 3.5 Fans and pumps

Unlike the components considered so far, fans and pumps are not essential parts of heat pumps. They are used to increase the circulation rates of air or liquid and play a major part in ensuring efficient operation, but a heat pump could be built without them. Their design requires minimization of their unwanted characteristics (energy use and noise) for the given flow rate and pressure-drop requirement. This can only be done by matching the fan or pump to the flow requirements and then matching the drive motor to the fan or pump characteristics at design conditions.

As air has a low heat capacity compared with liquids, the energy required for a fan to move a given quantity of heat is greater than that required by a liquid pump to move a similar quantity of heat, and in heat pump applications the choice of fans and fan motors is more critical to efficient operation than the choice of pumps.

The types of fans to be considered are centrifugal (forward or backward curved blades), vane or tube axial, propeller fans, or mixed flow fans (Fig. 3.13), and that chosen depends on the combination of pressure drop and flow rate, and on available space. The efficiency of fan impellers may be conveniently related to specific speed ($N_s$) defined as

$$N_s = NQ^{1/2}/p^{3/4},$$

where $N$ is rotational speed (rpm), $Q$ is air flow rate ($m^3 s^{-1}$) and $p$ is pressure drop for air at standard density (Pascals at 1.2 kg $m^{-3}$). As power delivered by a fan ($R$) is $Qp$ (ignoring velocity pressure changes), an equivalent alternative definition is

$$N_s = NQ^{5/4}/R^{3/4} \qquad \text{where } R = Qp,$$

showing that specific speed, for a given rotational speed, increases with increasing flow rate, and reduces with increasing power delivery. In the units quoted, the specific speeds at which various impeller types are most efficient are given in Table 3.4 [72]. 'Efficiency' is the proportion of the power supplied which is transmitted to the air flow. Backward-curved centrifugal fans are most efficient for low-flow, high-power applications and propeller

Centrifugal blower

Mixed-flow impeller

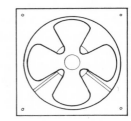
Axial fan

*Fig. 3.13* Fan types.

fans are best for high flows and low power. In intermediate ranges, flow geometry and impeller casing volume are likely to be the deciding factors.

Large, slow-running fans are both quieter and more efficient than smaller units providing the same air flow so that, subject to space and cost limitations, the largest fan with the most efficient type of impeller should be selected. Care should then be taken to ensure that the drive motor is efficient for the most likely running condition. However, motors provided by blower manufacturers are commonly chosen entirely on grounds of cost and reliability, particularly in smaller units and overall air-moving efficiencies of 20% or less are not uncommon.

For a given air path and blower unit, the flow and pressure obtained are uniquely determined by the intersection of the fan characteristic and system characteristic curves on a pressure-flow diagram (operating point) (Fig. 3.14). Fan characteristics for a range of operating speeds are provided by fan manufacturers but the system characteristic must be calculated for the particular application.

Pressure-drop characteristics of heat exchangers and of ducts may be readily calculated from standard handbooks, but calculation (or even measurement) of pressure-drops due to irregular obstructions of contorted air-flow paths is impracticable. The provision of smooth air flows thus both aids efficiency and makes possible proper matching of components (and also aids acoustic design) [73]), and should be one of the first considerations in designing heat pumps using air. Smooth flows in the impeller region will be ensured by the use of properly designed impeller housings but these can only work if their inlets and outlets are not unduly restricted.

The costs of operating heat pumps depend very much on the ease of maintenance and service. As both fans and pumps are vulnerable to accidental mechanical blockage and consequent motor burn-out, their siting (and in the case of pumps, valving), must be arranged so that straightforward service replacement is possible on installed equipment. Control circuits must also be designed to ensure that damage to fans or pumps has a minimum

*Table 3.4* Efficiency of blower units with various impeller types, after Kenny [72]

| Impeller type | Specific speed range for peak efficiency | Efficiency (%) |
| --- | --- | --- |
| Backward-curved centrifugal | 2.4–14 | 60–70 |
| Forward-curved centrifugal | 4.1–14 | 42–52 |
| Mixed flow | 5.2–21 | 50–60 |
| Vane axial | 17–62 | 65–72 |
| Tube axial | 34–70 | 50–55 |
| Propeller fan | 31–87 | 38–45 |

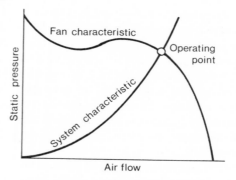

*Fig. 3.14* Fan and system characteristics.

effect on other parts of the heat pump system, particularly the relatively expensive compressor unit.

### 3.6 Pipes and joints

Piping is required to join the various components of the refrigeration circuit to each other and to contain the refrigerant (see Fig. 3.1, page 32). It must be leak-tight in order to contain the refrigerant and also to keep out contaminants such as moisture. Pipe diameters must be sufficient to avoid excessive pressure drops in the circuit and yet small enough to ensure adequate refrigerant flow velocities and oil circulation and return. Piping must be integrated with the heat exchangers and the refrigerant flow controller in a circuit which may contain additional components such as accumulators, liquid to suction heat exchangers, oil separators, valves, filter-dryers, shut-off and charging valves, sight glasses, and even flow-meters.

A simple circuit in which a single flow is taken to each component in turn is not always sufficient. In many complex circuits with variable capacity compressors or with multiple heat exchangers, the correct flow and pressure characteristics may only be obtainable by using double-pipe risers, in which one of two parallel pipes is closed by an oil trap at low refrigeration flow rates, and both risers are available for greater flows. Information on the design of such systems is available in the ASHRAE handbooks.

In the simple circuit, there are three basic piping connections, the vapour, liquid, and suction lines. The vapour line, carrying hot refrigerant vapour from the compressor to the condenser, will need to have the largest diameter in order to minimize pressure drops, its diameter being adequately specified by the compressor outlet connection in cases where the pipe run is short. (In the case of reversible units, both vapour and suction lines will require this diameter.) If this pipe work is exposed, thermal insulation will be necessary to retain heat energy and to avoid dangers from burns (particularly in the case of refrigerant 22 for which vapour temperatures in excess of 100°C are usual).

The main consideration in the liquid line (that between the condenser and evaporator and including the refrigerant flow controller) is the avoidance of pressure drops which could lead to excessive premature evaporation of refrigerant. This will be affected by both the amount of condenser subcooling and the amount of refrigerant in the circuit, and the overall combination must be checked over the full range of operating conditions for the heat pump. It is normal practice to include a sight glass and a filter dryer in the liquid line between the condenser and the flow controller. The sight glass allows visual inspection for unwanted vapour bubbles and thus helps to ensure that approximately the correct amount of refrigerant is present in the circuit. The filter dryer protects the flow controller from foreign particles which may block it and remove any water vapour which may be present. Between the flow controller and the evaporator, insulation is necessary on the pipework to prevent condensation and frosting, and this must be of a type not prone to water logging and consequent freezing.

The suction line between the evaporator and the compressor is the most critical pipe connection as it has to provide oil return to the compressor without risk of refrigerant liquid slugs damaging it. To capture excess liquid an accumulator is frequently included in this line, and a liquid to suction line heat exchanger may be used to increase both liquid subcooling and suction vapour superheating [74]. Once again a full range of operating conditions must be considered to ensure oil return at low refrigerant flow rates and to prevent liquid slugs developing at high flow rates. Generally the heat gained by an uninsulated suction line from its surroundings will be advantageous, as long as condensation of water on cold pipes poses no problems. Although a relatively small component of the total cost, the cost of piping (and the refrigerant to fill it and the insulation to cover it) may become significant in complex systems, and must be offset against the advantages of the smooth air flows achievable in systems with well-spaced components.

Copper tubing is universally used for halocarbon refrigerant circuits, as its combination of workability, strength and corrosion resistance is unmatched. Refrigerant quality tubing should be specified, which is usually supplied nitrogen-filled and sealed. Permanent joints must be brazed or silver soldered and openable connections must be flanged or flared to withstand normal operating pressures of 20 bar or more. The jointing standards required are higher than are necessary for hot-water services and special precautions must be taken to keep the interior of pipework clean and dry to avoid corrosive products developing during use. Refrigerant circuits should be opened to the atmosphere during service for as short a time as possible, to prevent moisture ingress and all air must be evacuated or flushed out of all pipework, including temporary service connections, as even a small amount of water vapour can react with the halocarbon refrigerant to form corrosive acids within the system. Where heat pumps are designed as two-part packages to be field connected, some manufacturers offer pre-charged, sealed vapour and liquid refrigerant lines in various lengths with which to make these connections. The end connectors are designed to provide a seal to the outside before breaking an internal seal connecting the refrigerant paths. Although these are not cheap, they can provide a more reliable installation than will normal field plumbing.

## 3.7 Refrigerant flow control

The high- and low-pressure sides of a vapour compression circuit must be separated by some type of flow restrictor acting as an expansion device. The practical difficulties of expanding the refrigerant at constant entropy through a work-recovering expander in a reverse Carnot cycle are not justified by the amount of work recovered, which typically could increase the heat available by less than 5%. Instead, the refrigerant is expanded at constant enthalpy, using a narrow orifice (which may take the form of a long capillary tube) in a Rankine cycle as described previously (Section 2.2).

In addition to providing the necessary pressure drop, the restrictor must serve to regulate the flow of refrigerant preventing both evaporator starvation and liquid return to the compressor. The range of conditions over which a heat pump operates produces changes in the density of the vapour returning to the compressor and in volumetric flow rate. These must be matched automatically by changes in flow through the restrictor. This can be achieved by either maintaining a given level of superheating in the vapour leaving the evaporator, or controlling the amount of subcooling in the liquid leaving the condenser, or using the self-regulating properties of the flow in a long, small-bore tube. In larger equipment, where excess refrigerant may be temporarily stored in accumulators, the refrigerant flow to the evaporator may be controlled by a float valve.

For small- and medium-sized equipment, control of the vapour superheat is the commonest method, and this is achieved by using a thermostatic expansion valve, often referred to as a TEV (Fig 3.15). This consists of an orifice (sited immediately before the evaporator) which may be partially or fully closed by a spring-loaded needle or plunger; a diaphragm connected to the plunger; and a sensing bulb connected via a capillary tube to the other side of the diaphragm. This bulb, which is located so as to sense the temperature of the vapour leaving the evaporator, contains a liquid/vapour mixture selected to increase the pressure in the bulb and the capillary (and thus on the diaphragm) when there is an increase in this vapour

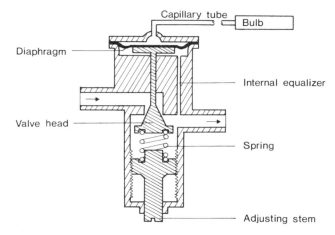

*Fig. 3.15* Thermostatic expansion valve.

temperature. The plunger side of the diaphragm is exposed to the liquid line refrigerant pressure at the entrance to the evaporator. The combination of spring pressure, bulb pressure, and line pressure is designed to control the refrigerant flow to maintain a fixed vapour superheat at the sensing bulb. An increase in superheat results in an increased bulb pressure, which depresses the diaphragm, opens the valve, and increases the refrigerant flow. A decrease in superheat has the reverse effect. If the fluid in the bulb is correctly matched to the refrigerant in the circuit, the amount of superheat will be controlled for a wide range of operating conditions. Although ideally the amount of superheat is kept constant, in practice the amount of superheat increases as conditions depart from the design condition.

The necessity of providing sufficient superheat (about 5 K for R22) to operate the TEV necessitates an increased evaporator surface area, and if care is not taken in siting the sensor bulb, 'hunting' (successive under and over correction of the flow) can occur. Usually it is necessary to provide a bleed port to allow pressure equalization in the system during idle periods to minimize compressor starting torque. This port may also aid oil circulation. The use of thermistor sensors and electronic controls to operate a variable orifice expansion valve could overcome these difficulties, but to date this has not been generally accepted on grounds of cost and unproved reliability.

A device similar in principle to a TEV, but with a bulb sensing the liquid temperature leaving the condenser and a diaphragm sensing the pressure in the same liquid line, may be used to control the refrigerant flow in order to maintain a fixed amount of liquid subcooling in the condenser. Such a subcooling control valve is incorporated in the Westinghouse 'Hi-Re-Li' system which, it is claimed, extends the range of evaporating and condensing temperatures over which control is maintained with no loss of performance at design conditions. The system provides a drained condenser and a flooded evaporator for a wide range of evaporation temperatures thus ensuring maximum heat transfer efficiency and reducing the fall off in capacity at lower evaporation temperatures by comparison with a TEV [75].

Another alternative to the TEV is an electrically operated valve driven from an electronic controller. Given a suitable controller and appropriate temperature sensors a system operating at minimum superheat regardless of operating conditions can be designed. An experimental system has been described which shows appreciable performance advantages [61]. Control manufacturers are now providing suitable electrically operated valves.

A long, small-bore capillary tube can also be used to control refrigerant flow in smaller refrigeration plants and heat pumps, a device which, despite its simplicity and low cost, is capable of maintaining control over a range of conditions. Such a tube allows a greater mass flow of liquid than of vapour and is designed so that at the specified load only liquid refrigerant enters the tube. As pressure falls along the tube, evaporation starts to occur at some point, with vapour bubbles forming in the refrigerant flow. If the flow rate falls, due to a change in conditions in the rest of the circuit, the pressure drop along the capillary is reduced, the bubbles of vapour will not form so early, and as a consequence the flow through the capillary will increase to restore the circuit balance.

At design conditions, control by means of a capillary tube is preferable to control by a TEV as no superheating in the evaporator is necessary (a suction-to-liquid heat exchanger can provide more cheaply any superheat needed to prevent liquid refrigerant returning to the compressor). Away from design conditions, theoretical and experimental investigations using R12 refrigerant [76] have demonstrated that for changes in evaporator condition, capillary control is as effective as is the thermostatic expansion valve, but for changes in condenser conditions there is some loss of efficiency or of capacity. In space-heating applications, where condensing conditions are restricted to a narrow temperature band, capillary control should be the best, as long as results proved for R12 apply equally to other refrigerants. The disadvantages of capillary control are the lack of adjustment compared with a TEV (which means several different capillaries may need to be tried before the most suitable geometry for a particular heat pump design is found), the danger of blockage (reduced but not necessarily totally eliminated by incorporating a filter dryer in the circuit), and the sensitivity to quality control of the small diameter tubing. Typical capillary bores are between 1 and 2 mm. Preliminary capillary sizing charts are provided by ASHRAE for cooling applications and these can provide a starting point for heating application design. It is recommended that charts relating to required mass flow rates be used rather than the simpler but less reliable charts relating directly to heat extraction capacity and based on refrigeration experience.

## 3.8 Accumulators and intermediate heat exchangers

It is common practice to incorporate a simple heat exchanger between the liquid and suction lines of a vapour compression refrigeration machine. This transfers heat effectively from subcooled refrigerant liquid to the suction gas, eliminating the need for superheating in the evaporator and thus improving evaporator performance. This improvement may be greater in practice than theoretical calculations indicate [74], partly due to increased compression efficiency with higher superheat, and can have advantages in heat pumps as well as in refrigeration equipment. It is also useful in all but the smallest machines to incorporate a liquid accumulator in the suction line to eliminate the possiblity of liquid return to the compressor. At least two manufacturers have combined these components, incorporating a heat exchanger within the accumulator [77].

The use of liquid-to-suction line heat exchangers effectively provides a second evaporator, allowing the main evaporator to be operated in a flooded condition, with a consequent improvement in internal heat transfer, as is illustrated in Fig. 3.16. This improvement to the basic single-stage cycle has been combined with the use of a subcooling control valve and a manifold check valve in the patented Westinghouse 'Hi-Re-Li' system [75] which was developed in response to an Edison Electric Institute requirement and

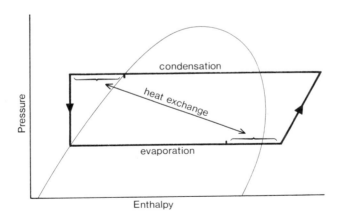

*Fig. 3.16* Effect of a suction – liquid heat exchanger.

which, it is claimed, gives improved performance and reliability.

Liquid/suction heat exchangers may be formed by simply running the two pipelines side by side and insulating them, or by carefully engineered counterflow heat exchangers, or in smaller systems by wrapping part of the refrigerant control capillary around the suction line. The latter expedient may improve the control characteristics of the capillary. If suction-line accumulators are used, oil return must be considered either by draining the accumulator to the compressor crankcase directly, or by providing means for oil and refrigerant liquid to be drawn out of the accumulator vapour outlet. Suitable accumulators, which should be large enough to hold half the total refrigerant charge as liquid, are readily available [78].

### 3.9 Defrosting

Whenever air is used as a heat pump heat source and evaporating temperatures fall below 0°C, frost will form on the heat exchanger as water is frozen out of the moist air. The rate of frost formation will depend on the temperature and humidity of the air, the evaporation temperature, and the coil design. Although a small amount of moisture or frosting may even improve coil performance by roughening the heat exchange surfaces [79], substantial amounts of frost will increase the thermal resistance. In air coils it will also increase air pressure drop, giving a reduced performance [80] and if nothing is done to remove the frost, the coil will become completely blocked. There are a number of well-established defrosting methods in use in the refrigeration industry [81], most of which are directly applicable to heat pumping applications. The objective must be to remove frost economically and quickly without endangering the reliability of the components, particularly the compressor. In larger units, it is usual to close a liquid-line solenoid valve and collect the refrigerant in the condenser and an accumulator prior to defrosting, in order to avoid the possibility of excess liquid being drawn into the compressor at the end of the defrost cycle. In smaller, packaged equipment, this is not usually necessary as long as some thought is given to compressor protection when designing the circuit.

The simplest approach to defrosting is to avoid frost in the first place. This is practicable for ventilation-heat-recovery heat pumps, in that a by-pass can be provided to keep some of the exhaust air away from the evaporator when it is too cold [82], but is not applicable to the majority of heat pump systems. Two evaporators for alternate use could be incorporated in the refrigeration circuit, one defrosting while the other is in use, but this is an expensive method which can only work above 0°C air temperature [83]. It has been suggested that frost could be avoided by using specially treated heat exchanger surfaces on which frost cannot form, but no suitable treatments have been demonstrated. At air temperatures above 2–3°C, stopping the compressor and allowing the air to melt the frost can be sufficient – this is known as off-cycle air defrost. At lower air temperatures, a positive method of frost removal is necessary, the two commonest being direct electric heating or the use of hot refrigerant gas. In all positive methods air circulation over the coil should be stopped during defrosting.

Electric defrosting usually uses heaters either fixed against or embedded in the heat exchange coil. As frost forms more thickly towards the bottom of air coils, the heating is usually graded so that it is more powerful there than elsewhere. The heating power is generally such that the compressor must be switched off before the heater comes on to avoid excessive combined electric current demands. A variation on this method is to circulate warm air, heated electrically or otherwise, across the coil to melt the frost.

In the methods described so far the frost has been melted by heat applied to the outside. In hot-gas defrost the frost is melted by heat applied internally by supplying hot refrigerant gas to the evaporator. This method uses less heat to remove a given amount of frost, and can be done in one of two ways.

In reverse-cycle defrost, a refrigerant circuit valve is used to change over the evaporator and the condenser. This reverse-cycle method provides rapid and effective defrosting. Energy use during reverse-cycle defrosting was monitored in the US in Edison Electric Institute trials in the 1960s showing that 0.5% of the total energy consumption was used [84]. More recent trials in climates with a higher defrost frequency show that up to 2% of the total energy consumed was used for defrosting, still a small proportion of the total energy (see Table 3.5). (These figures do not include the possible energy losses due to reduced heat transfer across partly frosted coils. Nor do they include the energy used by the supplementary heaters which may be operated during the defrosting operation to maintain heat supply.)

However, the pressure changes in the circuit at the point of changeover and the consequent lubrication and motor cooling problems can produce considerable stresses on the compressor. For reversible heat pumps, reverse cycle defrost is little different from the normal changeover from heating to cooling and a suitably protected compressor should be available. For heating-only heat pumps, the use of reverse-cycle defrosting could make greater demands on the compressor than does normal operation, and either direct electric defrost or an alternative hot-gas method should be used.

Hot-gas defrost, without cycle reversal, may be achieved by opening a condenser by-pass line, thus supplying hot gas from the compressor directly to the frosted evaporator. Under very cold conditions this may require the introduction of an additional restrictor after the evaporator to ensure a high enough condensing temperature during defrost. As always, some method of preventing liquid return to the compressor must be incorporated.

Various 'latent heat defrost' systems have been proposed. In refrigeration

*Table 3.5* Annual defrost requirements

| Site and period | Total defrost | | Compressor and fan energy use | | |
| | Cycles | Time (h) | Total (kWh) | During defrost | |
| | | | | (kWh) | (%) |
|---|---|---|---|---|---|
| Oxted 13.10.73–25.10.74 | 1612 | 108.3 | 14 092 | 161 | 1.14 |
| Alton 1.11.74–3.11.75 | 1266 | 50.3 | 13 100 | 262 | 2.00 |
| Capenhurst 14.1.74–13.1.75 | >1300 | 44.5 | 10 354 | 157 | 1.52 |

equipment the heat produced in the refrigeration cycle is normally waste, but it may be stored either in water or in liquid refrigerant and then used for defrosting. One defrosting system is operated by refrigerant pressure differentials without using the compressor [85]. In heat pumping applications the heat produced is not waste and such methods have less attraction.

Several other methods of defrosting have been proposed. In designs in which multiple evaporators are an essential part, each can be taken out of use in turn to defrost. Warm water can be run over the coil to remove ice (but this can only be recommended if there is a ready supply of waste warm water), and mechanical scraping [86] has also been proposed but has not, to the author's knowledge, been proved satisfactorily.

Whatever methods of defrosting are used, defrost water must be taken away, and in many climates this requires heated drain lines to prevent ice blockages, using low-power electric heaters along the lines. A minimum slope of 1:50 is recommended for effective drainage. If a defrost system uses automatically operated valves, it is essential to avoid liquid trapping in lines which could heat up and reach excessive pressures (100 bar is quoted as quite possible in a trapped liquid line [81]).

### 3.9.1 Defrosting controls

Once a defrosting system is chosen, controls to start and end the defrost cycle must be specified. The simplest method is time control, defrosting for a few minutes every hour or two of compressor operation. The amount of defrosting required depends on air conditions as illustrated in Fig. 3.17, which has been derived from data presented by Ambrose [87]. Experience has shown that defrost control systems which give typically 400 defrost cycles per year in a continental climate [84, 88] may give three times this number of defrost cycles in a more temperate maritime climate [89]. Thus if winter conditions are relatively steady and temperatures are consistently well below 0°C, time control may be adequate, but if conditions vary around the 0°C level (and especially if humidities are high), a more sophisticated control system is necessary to avoid excessive defrost operation at times other than the worst icing conditions.

As defrosting is necessary to maintain heat transfer performance, the most precise methods of defrost initiation sense a fall in this performance, using increased coil-to-air temperature difference, increased air-pressure drop across the coil, or increased fan power. Defrosting may be initiated by refrigerant temperature or pressure sensors, or a combination of both, possibly in conjunction with a timer, and may be terminated by a given temperature or pressure in the evaporator [90]. Frost detection by means of electrical capacitance measurement between suitably placed plates is also being considered [91].

Developments in electronic control systems are likely to lead to more complex control cycles. One manufacturer has proposed a microprocessor-based defrost controller not only using conventional combined temperature and pressure defrost initiation but also incorporating defrost initiation every 6 h when the outdoor temperature is low (even if no defrost is demanded by the sensors), a 10 min maximum defrost time, and a minimum 15 min between defrosts. To protect against wind gusts, the pressure initiation only operates if the required pressure is held for most of a 2 min period. If electronic controls are used the method of defrosting can be selected depending on the outdoor air temperature. For example off-cycle air or direct electric defrost can be chosen depending on whether the air is above

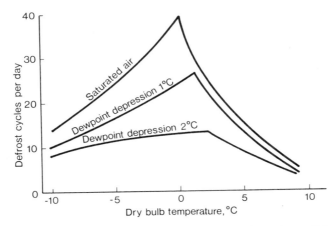

*Fig. 3.17* Variation of defrost frequency with outdoor air conditions.

or below a preset temperature in the 2–5°C range, giving a consequent reduction in defrost energy use.

Although defrost methods must be as energy efficient as possible, experience has shown that reliability must be the first consideration [84, 92, 93], both for the defrost equipment and the controls, and for the effects they have on the compressor and other components. Increasing the effectiveness of defrost systems without reducing reliability has been a major consideration of heat pump manufacturers for many years, and although the available systems are effective, there is still scope for improvement.

## 3.10 Other controls

The control of refrigerant flow and the control of defrosting on air-source heat pumps, which have been discussed above, are only two aspects of the overall heat pump control requirement. In addition to these, controls are needed which may be classified into three groups according to their function: protective devices, devices to improve efficiency, and operational controls to make the equipment actually work.

Protective devices are of two basic types – those that protect the total installation from being a hazard to people and those that minimize the costs of correcting malfunctions. The first type are generally required in order to meet national or local safety standards. It must not be possible for the heat pump equipment to have a high voltage at an accessible point or for it to cause a fire if any component or any reasonable combination of components fails. Primarily this requires the adequate earthing of casings and fusing of cables, and the provision of safety cut-outs in areas where high temperatures are possible, for example near supplementary heaters.

Although safety devices are an essential part of the equipment, devices to minimize the internal damage caused by component failures are not. Thus the extent to which they are used varies considerably for different applications and between different manufacturers. Reliability and low maintenance costs are essential if heat pumps are to be successful, so that it is important to consider incorporating controls to aid this.

The compressor is usually the most expensive and most vulnerable component in a heat pump and so requires the best protection. It is vulnerable to refrigerant circuit blockage, loss of refrigerant, failure of the pumps or fans which move the heat distributing medium, and excessively high or low electricity supply voltages. It can be protected by incorporating both a cut-out to sense high temperatures or high current in the compressor motor windings and a high-pressure cut-out to isolate the compressor in the event of an excess discharge pressure. Such cut-outs should be arranged so that a service engineer must inspect the equipment before they can be reset, as otherwise there is a danger that the equipment will continue to operate in an incorrect manner until there is a more serious failure. Additional compressor protection may include a low-pressure cut-out on the suction line, a filter in the refrigerant circuit, an accumulator to hold excess refrigerant, and a crankcase heater to prevent accumulation of refrigerant liquid in the compressor crankcase, although the latter three are not strictly speaking 'controls'. Devices to prevent the compressor restarting within 2 or 3 min of stopping are also fairly common to ensure that the compressor starts with the refrigeration circuit at a uniform pressure, minimizing the compressor load at start up.

Control devices whose function is wholly or primarily to improve operating efficiency or equipment life include oil return devices, speed or capacity controls, and starting controls. Oil return devices can be oil separators, which prevent compressor oil being pumped all round the circuit and return it directly from vapour to suction line, or positive oil return pipes from the bottom of suction-line accumulators. The use of speed controls applied to fans or pumps in conjunction with capacity controls on compressors can give improved efficiencies at part-load conditions even greater than those discussed in Section 3.3. For electric motors, starting controls of some type will be necessary. These may be conventional motor starters for large motors, or for smaller applications they may be time delay relays which reduce starting current by preventing simultaneous starting of fans and compressors. For single-phase units, resistive soft-start devices may be used (see Section 4.1.3). On large installations incorporating many small heat pumps, time delay relays are used to reduce starting current requirements for the whole installation by randomizing the start time of the individual units over a period of perhaps 1 or 2 min after the system is switched on. In areas where there are substantial numbers of heat pumps, such delay relays may be specified by the electricity supply authority in order to ensure a smooth return after supply failure.

Operational controls are necessary to make the system operate as the designer wishes. In reversible heat pumps which can provide either heating or cooling, either a refrigerant reversing valve or a means for reversing the flow of the heat distribution medium is required. Reversible units also require either two refrigerant flow control devices (for example one thermostatic expansion valve and one capillary or else two of either) or some device which controls from conditions in the liquid line. Reversing valves or solenoid valves are also required to control defrosting cycles and pump down conditions.

In addition to controls within the heat pump, there will be external controls to operate both the heat pump and any subsidiary equipment. One or more thermostats (or in some applications humidity controllers) will be required, together with possible additional controls on heat emitters in the heat distribution circuit. If heating is provided by a combination of heat pump and supplementary heating, it may be important to ensure that if one heat source fails it automatically brings on the other, and that the user of the equipment is made aware of it immediately by some warning signal.

The development of electronic controls for heat pumps allows more complex protective arrangements to be incorporated relatively easily. In one case an air-source heat pump has a control circuit which monitors the relation between defrost time and compressor running time and gives a warning if the defrost time is excessive. The incorporation of micropro cessors in control systems permits the use of almost any type of control function which can be adequately defined. To date most microprocessor heat pump controls have done little more than copy the operation of conventional controls. This situation could change rapidly and future heat pumps could incorporate a sophisticated fault-diagnosis system together with more selective protection devices. The larger the heat pump unit, the more comprehensive the protective controls that will be justified to avoid high repair costs.

### 3.11  Overall design optimization

Once a heat pump application has been specified, the design of suitable equipment requires co-ordination of all the component parts discussed above. The final result must be efficient, reliable, and economic, and the combination of a number of different but inter-related components to these ends is a complex problem.

In many cases, the operating conditions for a heat pump are close enough to those for refrigerating equipment for designs and practices of the refrigeration industry, which has many years of proved practical experience, to be appropriate or at least a sound starting point. The basic procedure starts with the selection of a refrigerant and of a compressor with an appropriate capacity, followed by calculation of heat exchanger sizes, leading finally to choice of suitable controls. The interactions between heat exchangers, compressor, controls, and refrigerant are such that, starting from scratch, much experimentation would normally be required in addition to design calculations, before a satisfactory design could be achieved. To avoid this, the design process for new applications may be carried out using computer modelling techniques. If a range of possible components can be specified, whose individual characteristics are known, then the computer is well able to evaluate the interactions resulting from different combinations of components, and optimize the design parameters by choosing the best combination for the full range of operating conditions.

Computer modelling of heat pumps has been used at varying levels of complexity, in the simpler cases the input data being taken from manufacturers' catalogues, and in the most complex models, using detailed mathematical equations defining the physics of every part (even down to compressor valve springs). More complex models are potentially more useful, but are also more prone to serious error if underlying assumptions do not quite match the physical reality. Examples of the use of computer modelling of heat pumps are to be found in the literature [58, 94–98]. Particular components which have been modelled include evaporators [99], capillary tubes [100], refrigerants [101] and compressors [102].

In most applications the parameters to be optimized will be clear – the best performance over a given range of conditions within a given cost, or else the lowest cost unit to provide a given performance. In systems which must provide either heating or cooling from a single reversible heat pump, the optimization problem is more acute, as the best design for one application will be appreciably different from the best design for the other. (The basic reason for this is that cooling requires a large drop in the indoor air temperature in order to dehumidify effectively and heating requires a small temperature rise to give a good c.o.p. A single indoor heat exchanger cannot meet both these criteria.) This problem can be resolved by optimizing for only one of the operating modes or by assessing minimum total cost based on the expected operating times in each mode over the life of the equipment. Optimizing overall may be appropriate for large, individually designed heat pumps, but not for mass-produced units for which the pattern of use may be unpredictable. Most, if not all, reversible heat pumps are optimized for cooling with a consequent loss of heating efficiency, although in some countries there have been moves towards reversible units designed primarily for efficient heating [62].

In optimizing a heat pump design it is not only necessary to decide the best sizes of the various components; it is also necessary to choose which components are actually required. The possible use of accumulators and intermediate heat exchangers in particular gives considerable scope for choice, as a survey of air-to-air heat pumps on the French market has revealed [77]. There is no best solution and the advantages of one solution may outweigh its disadvantages in a particular application. Generally, the more complex the solution the more efficient it is but the more expensive and possibly less reliable.

For units having either the heat source or the heat requirement dependent on the weather, the climate will have an appreciable effect on the design. Equipment designed for one type of climate may require redesign before it is suitable for use in another, and this is true for economic climates as well as for the meteorological sort.

## 3.12 Reliability

Although heat pumps generally have lower energy costs than alternative equipment providing both cooling and heating, they are more expensive to purchase, so it is important that repair and maintenance charges should not make total operating costs uncompetitive. Severe reliability problems were experienced in the US in the 1950s and 1960s with heat pumps for housing, and this had led to a poor reliability image for heat pumps generally. The extent of the US problem was such that their use was banned by the Defence Department for Military housing as from 1964 [103]. A research project was initiated in 1963 by Edison Electric Institute, to seek heat pump improvements [84]. Two manufacturers were each asked to produce 200 improved prototype units for evaluation in fully monitored trials by 57 utilities.

The units produced were a 10.6 kW Westinghouse single-phase residential unit and a 17.6 kW Carrier three-phase unit intended primarily for commercial use. Both were installed to suit the building cooling load with supplementary heaters to make up the heating capability as necessary. The prototypes were operated and monitored over periods of at least a year, many for 4 or 5 years, as part of the research project with particular emphasis on maintenance requirements. Comprehensive data handling procedures were devised to ensure the collection of data in a readily analysable form.

Service records showed that the residential units needed an average of 1.13 service calls per unit year and the commercial units needed 0.78 calls. In both cases the average call required 3 h labour. Over 60% of the calls were in the heating season. Controllers, capacitors, fan belts, and relays were the most frequent causes of failure. It was felt that reliability had been improved compared with 'first generation' heat pumps of the previous decade, but that there was still room for further improvement.

The work done by manufacturers to remedy the reliability problems resulted in improved heat pumps appearing in the US in the late 1960s [93], and these became sufficiently well proved for the Defense Department restriction to be removed in 1975. A survey in 1973 [104] relating to the Seattle area showed an improving trend in heat pump repair costs and, based on the available experience, the total repair and maintenance costs of heat pumps and of competitive systems in the Seattle area are shown in Table 3.6. For each of the systems considered, the relationship of repair costs to puchase cost was similar (the cost difference between the heat pump and the electric furnace and air-conditioning combination seems high). Detailed user comments in the survey showed that the general level of heat pump reliability was acceptably good, although further improvement would be welcome.

A maintenance cost schedule was developed for a small air-to-air reversible heat pump as part of the very detailed ACES study carried out for the US Department of Energy (see Chapter 5). This gave the following figures over a 20-year lifetime for a heat pump of 7.2 kW heating capacity at 8.3°C ambient. The basic purchase price excluding installation was $1080 [105].

Table 3.6 Repair and maintenance costs, Seattle, 1973

| System | Mean annual repair and maintenance cost ($) | Purchase cost ($) | Repair and maintenance as % of purchase cost (%) |
|---|---|---|---|
| Heat pump | 102.76 | 3219 | 3.2 |
| Electric furnace | 33.60 | 1186 | 2.8 |
| Gas furnace | 40.60 | 985 | 4.1 |
| Oil furnace | 38.55 | 1184 | 3.3 |
| Electric furnace plus air-conditioning | 62.61 | 2322 | 2.7 |

| | |
|---|---|
| Annual routine service | $20 p.a. |
| Annual service costs | $30 p.a. in years 4, 16. |
| | $50 p.a. in years 6, 12, 18. |
| Electrical system | $120 in year 13. |
| Compressor replacement | $650 in years 8, 16. |

This gives a total maintenance cost over 20 years of $2030 or on average approximately 10% of the purchase price of the unit per year

In order to examine the scope for further improvement, it is necessary to consider reliability data in more detail. A survey in 1976 in the US [70] showed that although average reliability was good, some particular units were far from reliable. In a sample of 133 installations of assorted heat pumps, the frequency of service calls was as shown in Table 3.7. The 86% of owners having less than one call per year had cause to be satisfied, but the two owners averaging six per year (over 2- and 4-year periods respectively) would have real grounds for complaint. This uneven distribution shows the importance of insurance or guarantee schemes to spread the load of repair costs uniformly across customers, and emphasizes the need to have well-established networks of service and maintenance engineers.

From the designer's viewpoint, it is necessary to split the data according to types of failure. This was done in the tests conducted by the Edison Electric Institute on the specially designed units for residential and commercial use and has also been done by American Electric Power Service Corporation (AEP) [107] for a wider range of equipment from five manufacturers over a 10-year period. A third study was based on the experience of the Alabama Power Company (APC) with a 10-year heat pump service contract scheme covering some 5000 installations [104]. It is seen that in 15 years of use the average heat pump could be expected to experience five refrigeration circuit failures, four control failures, four fan and motor failures, and one compressor failure. Fifteen years corresponds to around 40 000 h operation and this

*Table 3.7* Frequency of service calls [106]

| No. of installations | Average no. of calls per year |
|---|---|
| 62 | less than 0.25 |
| 52 | 0.25–1.0 |
| 11 | 1.0–2.0 |
| 6 | 2.0–3.0 |
| 2 | 6.0 |
| Total 133 | Overall average 0.63 |

represents a high degree of overall reliability compared with automobile engines and other mass-produced machinery.

The AEP study showed also how failure rates compared between five (unnamed) manufacturers over the years 1971 to 1973. Although some components are equally troublesome for all manufacturers, and in this study failure of three-phase fan units was a conspicuous problem, compressors in particular show a wide difference in reliability between manufacturers. One manufacturer's lowest compressor failure rate was over 22% per unit year, whereas another manufacturer's highest rate was less than 7%. This wide variation between manufacturers is also seen in the APC data [108], in which six manufacturers are named as having high compressor reliability compared with all others. High reliability is associated with manufacturers who have used compressors specially developed for heat pump duty, rather than using standard air-conditioning units, as the standard air-conditioning unit may not be designed for the full range of evaporating and condensing pressures which heat pumps (and particularly reversible units) have to meet.

A more recent study of AEP data [109] shows that even the better manufacturers have continued to improve reliability to the extent that service costs can be less than US$50 per year. Some components still produce failures which could be avoided, fan motors and compressor controls particularly need more consideration.

A Canadian study by Ontario Hydro of 300 heat pumps installed in 1973–74 and examined in 1975–7 showed poor reliability [110] and highlighted the need for more recent improved designs for cooler climates. Problems with installation and customer education accounted for more than a quarter of service calls in 1975/6, and the defrost circuit was the most troublesome item. The following year, fans were the major problem, with defrost circuits and compressors close behind.

A French study of several hundred small heat pumps, probably mostly installed for ventilation heat recovery, showed many problems to be due to faulty installation [111]. This and other studies show clearly that the levels of training for installers need to be improved in Europe, and probably everywhere except the US. American manufacturers importing into Europe are accepting this, and at least one manufacturer has trailer-mounted mobile training centres for heat pump technicians. European manufacturers should take note. There is increasing interest in heat pumps in British polytechnics and technical colleges, which hopefully will produce more trained engineers aware of heat pumps, and there is an increasing range of educational equipment available to demonstrate heat pump principles. One example is shown in Fig. 3.18.

The American pattern for mass-produced heat pumps has been as follows. Sales; problems; development over a 20-year period; and finally proved solutions by some (but not all) manufacturers. Other countries in which heat pumps are not yet established should study American experience and be

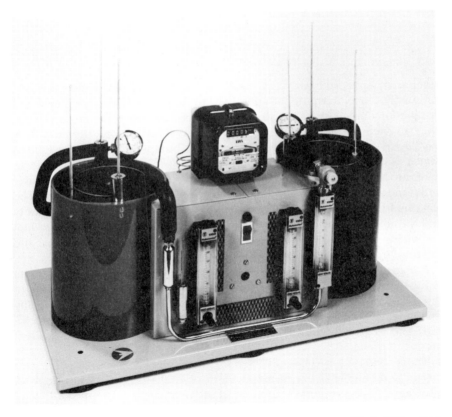

*Fig. 3.18* Mechanical heat pump teaching equipment. Courtesy of P. A. Hilton Ltd.

able to produce reliable units without going through the early reliability problems on a large scale, although some development to meet different climate requirements will be needed. The scope for both very good and for rather poor reliability, depending upon the level of care and skill in design, has been demonstrated, and it is up to purchasers to demand properly designed equipment. The smaller and the less expensive the heat pump the greater the cost of maintenance as a proportion of total costs and the more important is the need for 'designed-in' reliability.

Once sound equipment has been purchased and installed, its reliability is dependent on proper maintenance. If there are air filters, they must be cleaned or changed regularly, and refrigeration components and controls should be checked at least annually. Regular cleaning of heat exchangers must be planned. Whilst these present no problems for small numbers of large machines, where there are large numbers of small machines this necessitates the training and use of considerable numbers of skilled technicians. The setting up of appropriate service organizations must be the forerunner of quantity sales of any type of heat pump.

### 3.13 Standards and specifications

Standards, specifications, and codes of practice are produced locally, nationally, and internationally in order to help ensure that products and installations are both safe and effective. As they are generally produced after a given product has started to gain general acceptance, the most fully developed set of standards relating to heat pumps is that of the United States. Although US standards can form a basis for those of other nations, there are relevant differences in practice between countries, and local codes and standards must always be adhered to where they exist. Standards may be classified broadly into three possible types. The first type concerns safety and the ability to function, the second type is specific to one type of product and yields rating and performance data under full load test conditions, and the third provides data representative of operation in real applications.

For an electric, air-source, heat pump the first type of standard may relate to all electric appliances generally, or may be a code of practice relating to refrigeration or air-conditioning equipment, and need not include any specific reference to the heat pump. Such standards are in existence worldwide and frequently form the basis for the more specific standards for heat pumps.

The second type is well established for heat pump packages in the US, and provisional standards are in existence in several European countries and elsewhere. These provide a measure of the relative 'size' of units, and may give data at perhaps two conditions. They generally check operation under various extreme conditions but do not provide sufficient information to enable the potential user to differentiate meaningfully between different designs of the same size.

The third type of standard has yet to be developed for heat pumps other than in the US [112]. The effects of frosting and cycling on seasonal performance must be considered. For an air-to-air unit, frosting and cycling will both reduce performance compared with that indicated by a 'second type' standard, but for an air-to-water unit, cycling may actually improve performance [113]. Heat pump standards of this type can only be meaningful if they are related to specific heating systems, and testing to them could prove to be a relatively costly business. They do provide an impetus to manufacturers to meet the performance of the best of their competitors, whereas 'second type' standards can, once established, lead to a 'levelling down' to a generally acceptable performance level.

If any standard is to be of value it must be workable and must be based upon an agreed consensus by manufacturers and others based in turn on experience. For this reason, it is inevitable that standards develop slowly and the time from provisional draft to published specification can be many years.

### 3.13.1 *US standards and specifications*

Standards for heat pump performance were laid down in the US as long ago as 1948 [114], and have been developed and updated since then. A comprehensive listing of codes and standards from 38 US organizations is to be found in the American Society of Heating Refrigerating, and Air-conditioning Engineers (ASHRAE) handbook – *Fundamentals*, 1981, and the majority of the relevant standards are published by ASHRAE themselves, by Underwriters Laboratories, Inc. (UL), and by the Air-Conditioning and Refrigeration Institute (ARI). The scope of these standards may be judged from Table 3.8, in which the most important ASHRAE and UL and many of the relevant ARI standards are listed.

The 'Unitary heat pump specification for military family housing', published by the National Bureau of Standards (NBS), establishes comprehensive requirements for performance, testing, rating, design, safety, serviceability, and reliability of hermetic electric motor-compressor driven heat pumps in the 5–25 kW range and forms a good model for other specifications.

Standards for testing seasonal efficiency of unitary heat pumps have been developed by NBS [115] and these should soon be adopted by ASHRAE and ARI. These require performance measurements for at least three conditions representative of cold, warm and frosting conditions, and provide sufficient data for seasonal efficiency to be calculated once building-heat requirement and weather conditions are specified.

*Table 3.8* Some US standards relevant to heat pumps

| | |
|---|---|
| ASHRAE 37–78 | Methods of testing for rating unitary air conditioning and heat pump equipment. |
| UL–559 | Heat pumps. (A standard for safety for heat pumps up to 50 hp, excluding small room units.) |
| ARI 240–81 | Air-source unitary heat pump equipment. |
| ARI 260–75 | Application, installation, and servicing of unitary systems |
| ARI 320–76 | Water-source heat pumps. |
| ARI 340–82 | Commercial and industrial heat pump equipment. |
| ARI 380–78 | Packaged terminal heat pumps. |
| ARI 410–81 | Forced circulation air-cooling and air-heating coils. |
| ARI 495–74 | Refrigerant liquid receivers. |
| ARI 510–73 | Ammonia compressors and compressor units. |
| ARI 520–74 | Positive displacement compressor and condensing units. |
| ARI 550–77 | Centrifugal or rotary water-chilling packages. |
| ARI 560–75 | Absorption water-chilling packages. |
| ARI 590–76 | Reciprocating water-chilling packages. |
| ARI 710–71 | Liquid-line driers. |
| ARI 720–76 | Refrigerant access valves and hose connectors. |
| ARI 750–76 | Thermostatic refrigerant expansion valves. |

### 3.13.2 *European standards and specifications*

'Second type' standards are being developed or are in draft form in a number of European countries, and changes are sufficiently rapid for the interested reader to be well advised to check the current situation with the relevant national standards organizations. In West Germany, DIN 8957 includes heat pumps as air-conditioning systems and DIN 8900 covers heat pumps more specifically. Heat pumps are also covered in the German Society of Engineers heat recovery specification VDI-Richtlinie 2078, and the General Consultant for Electricity Use (HEA) has published specifications and definitions relating to heat pump fundamentals.

In France, AFNOR standards E 38 100, E 38 101 and E 38 110 provide definitions and test methods for heat pump rating tests. Draft specifications have been considered by the International Electrotechnical Commission (IEC) and by the International Council for Building Research Studies and Documentation (CIB).

In Britain, BS 3456: Part 2, Section 2.34 relates to safety of air-conditioners, and BS 4434 covers refrigeration safety. The latter is augmented for ammonia systems by an Institute of Refrigeration code of practice [116]. There is also a guide to good practice for air-conditioning including heat pumps, produced by the Heating and Ventilating Contractors Association. These represent the 'first type' standards.

'Second type' interim standards were produced in 1981 by the Air Conditioning Industry Approvals Authority [117, 118]. These interim standards have been accepted as the basis of a future British Standard. A combination of the Energy Conservation Act 1981 and of the formation of a HEVAC Association Heat Pump Group suggests that 'third type' standards may soon be considered. Although standards relating to general refrigeration equipment may suffice to ensure adequate safety of heat pump equipment, the development of high performance units, which are properly designed to match particular applications, requires specific heat pump standards such as those currently being considered.

## References

[1] Midgley, T. and Henne, A. L. (1930). 'Organic fluorides as refrigerants'. *Ind. & Eng. Chem.* **22** (5), 542.

[2] Döring, R. (1976). 'On refrigerants in heat pumps'. *Bulletin International Institute of Refrigeration Annexe* **1**, 673–80.

[3] Private communication from Du Pont de Nemours, Geneva, Switzerland.

[4] Downing, R. C. and Gray, J. B. (1972). 'R502 – a better heat pump refrigerant'. *Refrigeration and Air Conditioning* **75** (892), 45–6.

[5] Pfeiffenberger, U. (1982). 'Comparison of refrigerants'. *Int. J. Refrig.* **5** (2), 74–8.

[6] Watson, F. A., Abbas, S. P., Srinivasan, P. and Devotta, S. (1982). 'The thermal stability of R11 and R12B1 as high temperature heat pump working fluids'. In *International Symposium on the Industrial Application of Heat Pumps,* Coventry, UK. BHRA Fluid Engineering, Cranfield, UK, pp. 19–30.

[7] Almin, Y., Feuga, J. R. and Vuillaume, L. (1982). 'Experiments with R133a. A new refrigerant for high temperature heat pumps'. In *International Symposium on the Industrial Application of Heat Pumps,* Coventry, UK. BHRA Fluid Engineering, Cranfield, UK. pp. 31–40.

[8] Daniel, G., Anderson, M. J., Schmid, W. and Tokumitsu, M. (1982). 'Performance of selected synthetic lubricants in industrial heat pumps'. In *International Symposium on the Industrial Application of Heat Pumps,* Coventry, UK BHRA Fluid Enginering, Cranfield, UK, pp. 41–54.

[9] Giolito, F. and de Monevit, M. (1982). 'A synthetic lubricant for high temperature heat pumps'. In *International Symposium on the Industrial Application of Heat Pumps,* Coventry, UK. BHRA Fluid Engineering, Cranfield, UK, pp. 55–64.

[10] Bertinat, M. P., Drakesmith, F. R. and Taylor, B. J. (1982). 'The selection of a work fluid/lubricant combination for a high temperature heat pump dehumidifier' In *International Symposium on the Industrial application of Heat Pumps,* Coventry, UK. BHRA Fluid Engineering, Cranfield, UK, pp. 261–70.

[11] Kruse, H. and Jakobs, R. (1977). 'The importance of non-azeotropic binary refrigerants for use in heat pumps and refrigerating plant'. *Klima und Kalte Ing.* July/August, 253–60. (Translated as O.A. Trans. 1760, 1978, Electricity Council, London.)

[12] Haselden, G. G. and Klimek, L. (1957). 'An experimental study of the use of mixed refrigerants for non- isothermal refrigeration'. *Proc. Inst. Refrig.* **54**, 127–54.

[13] Kruse, H. (1981). 'The advantages of non-azeotropic refrigerant mixtures for

heat pump application.' *Int. J. Refrig.* **4** (3), 119–25.

[14] Rojey, A. (1980). *Pompe a chaleur fontionnant avec un melange de fluides* (Heat pumps operating with a mixture of fluids). Paper presented at the International Institute of Refrigeration, Commissions B1, B2, E1, E2, Mons, Belgium.

[15] Connon, H. (1981). *Estimation and application of thermodynamic properties for a non-azeotropic refrigerant mixture.* Paper presented at the International Institute of Refrigeration, Commissions B1, B2, E1, E2, Essen, West Germany, September 1981.

[16] Ackroyd, K. (1979), 'Safety aspects of chlorofluorocarbon refrigerants'. *Proc. Inst. Refrig.* **76**, 22–7.

[17] Anon. (1976). 'R–22 – your questions answered'. *Refrigeration and Air Conditioning* **79** (945), 27, 53.

[18] Spauschus, H.O. (1976). 'Technical considerations for refrigeration and air conditioning'. *ASHRAE J.* **18** (8), 23–4. Also other articles in same issue.

[19] H.M.S.O. (1976). *Chlorofluorocarbons and their effect on stratospheric ozone.* Pollution Paper No. 5, HMSO, London.

[20] Callis, L. B. (1979), 'Solar variability and ozone'. *New Scientist* **87**, 15 Nov., 532–4.

[21] Milbauer, P. (1981). *Further regulation of chlorofluorocarbons EPA's outlook.* Paper presented at the International Institute of Refrigeration, Commissions C2, D1, D2, D3, Boston, USA.

[22] Hudelson, G. D. (1981). *Industry attitude to further regulation of chlorofluorocarbons.* Paper presented at the International Institute of Refrigeration, Commissions C2, D1, D2, D3, Boston, USA.

[23] Ward, R. B. (1981). *The chlorofluorocarbon/ozone issue: goals of industry research program and recent scientific developments.* Paper presented at the International Institute of Refrigeration, Commissions C2, D1, D2, D3, Boston, USA.

[24] Reddy, D. W. (1979). 'The halocarbon contamination problem. Part II: Chlorofluorocarbons in the environment'. *Int. J. Refrig.* **2** (5), 181–4.

[25] Joyce, C. (1980). 'America clamps down on freons'. *New Scientist* **89**, 16 Oct., 142.

[26] Lorentzen, G. (1981). 'Official statement of the IIR on chlorofluorocarbons'. *Bull. IIR/IIF,* **61** (2), 320.

[27] Trias, P. F. (1981). 'Industry news: focus'. *ASHRAE J.* **23** (4), 19.

[28] Huttenlocker, D. F. (1976). 'Substitutes for current chlorofluorocarbon refrigerants in domestic appliances'. *ASHRAE J.* **18** (8), 33–7.

[29] Thrush, B. A. (1979). 'The halocarbon contamination problem. Part 1: Atmospheric effects of halocarbons'. *Int. J. Refrig.* **2** (5), 145–7.

[30] Newton, A. B. (1971). 'Variable speed inverter drives for compressors in air-conditioning systems'. *Proc. XIII Int. Cong. Refrigeration, Washington DC* **4**, 61–7.

[31] Eggert, L. J. (1962). 'Transient currents in heat pumps'. *ASHRAE J.* **4** (10), 50–3.

[32] Anon. (1977). 'Viel Interesse für die Motorheizung' (Much interest in motor-powered heating). *Oel und Gasfeuerung* **22** (6), 315.

[33] Ruhrgas AG (1977). *Europe's first gas heat pump put into operation in a swimming pool in Dortmund.* Translation No. T4306/BGC/1977, British Gas, London.

[34] Critoph, R. E. (1980). 'Fossil-fuel heat pumps for domestic, commercial and

industrial space heating'. *Proc. Inst. Electrical Engineers A* **127**(5), 326–9.

[35] Eiloart, T. (1977). 'Total-energy man'. *New Scientist* **76** (1079), 515–16.

[36] Didion, D., Maxwell, B. and Ward, D. (1977). *A laboratory investigation of a Stirling engine driven heat pump.* (Paper presented at UNESCO International Seminar, Heat and Mass Transfer in Buildings, Dubrovnik, Yugoslavia) August/September 1977.

[37] Sarkes, L. A., Nicholls, J. A. and Menzer, M. S. (1977). 'Gas fired heat pumps: an emerging technology'. *ASHRAE J.* **19** (3), 36–41.

[38] Walker, G., Fauvel, R., Gustafson, R. and van Bentham, J. (1982). 'Sterling engine heat pumps'. In *International Symposium on the Industrial Application of Heat Pumps*, Coventry, UK. BHRA Fluid Engineering, Cranfield, UK, pp. 9–18.

[39] Walker, G. (1980). *Stirling Engines*, Oxford University Press, Oxford, UK.

[40] Gaudenzi, P. (1979). *Rankine-cycle, vapour-driven engine for solar energy installations.* Paper presented at XV International Congress of Refrigeration, Venice, Italy, September 1979.

[41] Anon, (1976). 'Gas-energized heat pump to be developed'. *American Gas Association Monthly* September, 38.

[42] Angelino, G. (1976). 'Development of thermal prime movers for heat pump drive'. pp. 155–200 in: Camatini, E. and Kester, T. (1976). *Heat pumps and their contribution to energy conservation* Noordhoff, Leyden, Netherlands.

[43] Leach, S. J. (1977). 'Heat pump application in houses'. *Elektrowärme Int.* **35** (A5), A277–A283.

[44] Masters, J., Pearson, J. and Read, N. A. (1980). *Opportunities for gas engine driven heat pumps in the industrial and commercial markets,* Communication 1129, Institution of Gas Engineers, London.

[45] Suefuji, K., Itagaki, M., Murayama, A. and Harada, F. (1981). 'Development of a high efficiency refrigeration compressor'. *Int. J. Refrig.* **4** (5), 255–64.

[46] Rinck, Th. (1976). 'Wärmepumpenverdichter' (Heat pump compressors). *Elektrowärme Int.* **34** (A3), A131–A133.

[47] Zimmern, B. and Patel, G. C. (1974). 'Design and operating characteristics of the Zimmern single screw compressor'. *Purdue Compressor Technology Conference.*

[48] Chan, C. Y., Haselden, G. G. and Hundy, G. (1981). 'The Hallscrew compressor for refrigeration and heat pump duties'. *Int. J. Refrig.* **4** (5), 275–80.

[49] Constant, L. C. and Hundy, G. F. (1981). 'Compressors for heat pump application', *Institute of Chemical Engineers, North Western Branch Papers* No. 3, 4.1–4.9.

[50] Anon. (1978), 'ASHRAE highlights'. *Heating & Ventilating Review* April, 56–8.

[51] Anon. (1978), 'Rethinking refrigeration'. *Heating and Air-conditioning J.* **48** (55), 12–16.

[52] Ozu, M, and Itami, T. (1981). 'Efficiency analysis of power consumption in small hermetic refrigerant rotary compressors'. *Int. J. Refrig.* **4** (5), 265–70.

[53] Behrens, C. W. (1975), 'Open cycle air cooler operates without Freon'. *Appliance Manufacturer (USA)* April, 44–5.

[54] Schindelhauer, G. (1976). 'Der Wankel-kompressor – ein Wärmepumpen-verdichter?' (The Wankel compressor – a heat pump compressor?). *Elektrowärme Int.* **34** (A3), A133–A136.

[55] Reichelt, J. and Steimle, F. (1977). *Experimental investigations of a lubricated*

*compressor in comparison with an oil-free compressor by using several refrigerants for refrigerating plants and heat pumps.* Paper presented at International Institute of Refrigeration, Commissions B1, B2, E1, Belgrade, November 1977.

[56] Heap, R. D. (1978). 'Heat requirements and energy use in British houses'. *Energy and Buildings* **1** (4), 347–66.

[57] Paul, J., Schmitt, K. and Strehl, U. (1981). *Speed controlled heat pumps.* Paper presented at the International Institute of Refrigerations, Commissions B1, B2, E1, E2, Essen, West Germany, September 1981.

[58] Hiller, C. C. and Glicksman, L. R. (1976). *Improving heat pump performance via compressor capacity control.* PB–250592, US Department of Commerce, Washington DC.

[59] Douglass, E. S. (1976). 'Innovations in unitary heat pump designs'. *ASHRAE Trans.* **82** (1), 364–71.

[60] Westinghouse Electric Corporation (1977). *An investigation of methods to improve heat pump performance and reliability in a northern climate.* EPRI EM–319 (Research project 544–1), Electric Power Research Institute, Palo Alto, California.

[61] Tassou, S. A., Marquand, C. J. and Wilson, D. R. (1982). 'The effects of capacity modulation on the performance of vapour compression heat pump systems'. In *International Symposium on the Industrial Application of Heat Pumps*, Coventry, UK. BHRA Fluid Engineering, Cranfield, UK, pp. 179–86.

[62] Blundell, C. J. (1977). 'Optimizing heat exchangers for air-to-air space-heating heat pumps in the UK.' *Int. J. Energy Res.* **1** (1), 69–94.

[63] McAdams, W. H. (1954). *Heat transmission.* McGraw-Hill, New York.

[64] Kays, W. M. and London, A. L. (1954). *Compact heat exchangers.* McGraw-Hill, New York.

[65] Blundell, C.J. (1977). *A flat plate evaporator for domestic heat pumps.* ECRC/ N1077, Electricity Council Research Centre, Chester, UK.

[66] Bernier, J. (1981). *Intérêt des pompes de chaleur à transferts thermiques sans auxiliaires à convection naturelle et rayonnement (Interest in heat pumps operating without power for auxiliaries by using natural convection and radiation heat transfer).* Paper presented at International Institute of Refrigeration, Commissions B1, B2, E1, E2, Essen, West Germany, September 1981.

[67] Anon (1981). 'Energy fence as source for heat-pump installation'. *Building Services and Environmental Engineer* **3** (9), 10.

[68] Lorentzen, G. (1976). *The design of refrigerant recirculation systems.* Paper presented to Institute of Refrigeration, London, March 1976.

[69] Chaddock, J.B. (1976). 'Influence of oil on refrigerant evaporator performance'. *ASHRAE Trans.* **82** (1), 474–86.

[70] McMullan, J. T., Morgan, R. and Hughes, D. W. (1980). 'Development of domestic heat pumps' (EUR 7098). In *New ways to save energy. Proceedings of EEC seminar,* EEC, Brussels, p. 122.

[71] Carrington, C. G. (1977). *Optimizing a heat pump for heating purposes.* University of Otago, Dunedin, New Zealand.

[72] Kenny, R. J. (1968). 'Fans and blowers'. *Machine design* **40** (6), 152–73.

[73] Woods, R. I. (Ed.) (1972). *Noise control in mechanical services.* Sound Research Laboratories Ltd, Colchester, UK.

[74] Cooper, W. D. (1974). 'Refrigeration compressor performance as affected by

suction vapour superheating'. *ASHRAE Trans* **80** (1), 195–204.

[75] Biehn, G. L. (1970). *Design and operating cycle – single phase units*. Paper presented at ASHRAE Symposium; Heat pumps, improved design and performance, San Francisco, January 1970.

[76] Kovalczewski, J. J. (1961). 'Performance of refrigeration systems with fixed restrictions operating under variable evaporator and condenser conditions'. *J. Refrigeration* **4** (6), 122–8.

[77] Bernier, J. (1975). 'Air-air heat pumps'. *Revue Pratique du Froid et du Conditionnemènt d'Air* **28** (378), 69–83. (Translated as O.A. Trans. 2004, 1975, Electricity Council, London.)

[78] Grahl, D. R. (1982). 'Heat pump feature'. *Air conditioning and heat recovery* **85** (1008), 52 and 54.

[79] McQuiston, F.C. (1976). 'Heat, mass and momentum transfer in a parallel plate dehumidifying exchanger'. *ASHRAE Trans.* **82** (2), 87–106.

[80] Parken, W. H., Beausoleil, R. W. and Kelly, G. E. (1977). 'Factors affecting the performance of a residential air-to-air heat pump'. *ASHRAE Trans.* **83** (1), 839–49.

[81] Niederer, D. H. (1975). 'Defrosting of air units in central systems'. *ASHRAE Trans.* **81** (2), 581–91.

[82] Société Générale de Constructions Electriques et Méchaniques (1971). *Improvements in or relating to methods of and apparatus for air-conditioning a building.* British Patent 1360072.

[83] Cie Gen de Chauffe (1979). *Heat pump for central heating*. British Patent 1554759.

[84] Edison Electric Institute (1971). *Heat pump improvement research project final report*. EEI Publication No. 71–901, New York.

[85] Baulch, P. (1971). 'The latent heat defrost system'. *Refrigeration and Air Conditioning.* **74** (878), 49–50.

[86] Anon. (1975). 'Ice-free evaporator for heat pumps'. *Electrical Review* **197** (14), 427–8.

[87] Ambrose, E. R. (1966). *Heat pumps and electric heating*, Wiley, New York.

[88] Ambrose, E. R. (1974). 'The heat pump: performance factor, possible improvements'. *Heating, Piping and Air Conditioning* May, 77–82.

[89] Heap, R. D. (1977). 'American heat pumps in British houses'. *Elektrowärme Int.* **35** (A2), A77–A81.

[90] Dicker, C. S. (1978). 'Controls for heat pumps'. *Refrigeration and Air Conditioning* **81** (961), 120–3.

[91] Buick, T. R., McMullan, J. T., Morgan, R. and Murray, R. B. (1978). 'Ice detection in heat pumps and coolers'. *Int. J. Energy Res.* **2**, 85–98.

[92] Moore, P. B. (1976). 'There need not be another heat pump fiasco'. *Air Conditioning Heating and Refrigerating News* 16 February, 8–9.

[93] Anon. (1974). 'The heat pump rebirth'. *Electric Comfort Conditioning J. (USA)* January, 8–11.

[94] James, R. W., Marshall, S. A. and Saluja, S. N. (1976). 'The heat pump as a means of utilising low grade heat energy', *Building Services Engineer* **43**, January, 202–6.

[95] Takeda, H. (1974). *The year round simulation of air source heat pump*. Paper presented at 2nd symposium, 'The use of computers for environmental engineering related to buildings'. Paris, June 1974.

[96] Sundell, J. and Bubenko, J. A. (1980). 'Heat pump applications to single family dwellings – an analysis by computer model'. *Proc. Inst. Electrical*

*Engineers A* **127** (5), 320–5.

[97] Bildstein, P., Hamam, Y. and Ehrhart, J. (1980). 'Heat pump models for microprocessor based control systems' (EUR 7046). In *New ways to save energy. Proceedings of EEC Seminar*, EEC, Brussels, p. 164.

[98] Chi, J. and Didion, D. (1982). 'A simulation model of the transient performance of a heat pump'. *Int. J. Refrig.* **5** (3), 176–84.

[99] Hodgett, D. L. (1977). *Dehumidifying evaporators for high temperature heat pumps*. Paper presented at International Institute of Refrigeration, Commissions B1, B2, E1, Belgrade, November 1977.

[100] Maczek, K. and Krolieki, Z. (1981). *Non-adiabatic process in throttling capillary tube used in packaged refrigeration*. Paper presented at International Institute of Refrigeration. Commissions B1, B2, E1, E2, Essen, W. Germany, September 1981.

[101] Heide, R., Lippold, H. and Nowotny, S. (1980). *The determination of data of operating substances used in refrigeration and climatic engineering and their computer tailored representation*. Paper presented at International Institute of Refrigeration, Commissions B1, B2, E1, E2, Mons, Belgium, September 1980.

[102] MacLaren, J. F. T., Kerr, S. V. and Transchek, A. B. (1974), 'Modelling of compressors and values'. *Proc. Inst. Refrig.* **71**, 42–59.

[103] Halmos, E. E. (1975). 'Defense Dept. withdraws ban'. *Air Conditioning, Heating and Refrigeration News* 8 September, 1, 4.

[104] Blacklaw, J. R. and Johnson, B. M. (1973). *A study of energy conservation for the Seattle area through the use of heat pumps for comfort conditioning*. Battelle Pacific Northwest Laboratories, Richland, Washington.

[105] Abbatiello, L. A., Nephew, E. A. and Ballou, M. L. (1981). *Performance and Economics of the ACES and Alternative Residential Heating and Air Conditioning Systems in 115 US Cities,* ORNL/CON-52, Oak Ridge National Laboratory, Tennessee, USA.

[106] Rosenberg, R. M. (1976). 'A customer's view of the heat pump'. *Electrical World* **185** (5), 46–7.

[107] Anon. (1974). 'Heat pump data show service variations'. *Electrical World* **182** (9), 89–91.

[108] Lovvern, N. C. (1975). 'Utility details its heat pump service data'. *Electrical World* **183** (6), 148–9.

[109] Gorzelnik, E. F. (1978). 'Heat pumps get high grades up north'. *Electrical World* Sept. 15, 142–4, 192.

[110] Young, D. J. (1979). 'Utility sponsored heat pump research in Canada'. In *Heat pump and space conditioning systems for the 1990s,* Carrier Corporation, Syracuse, NY, pp. 49–58.

[111] Uniclima (1980). 'La fiabilité des pompes à chaleur' (The viability of heat pumps). *Chaud, Froid, Plomb* **34** (403), 71–5.

[112] ASHRAE 116P, *Methods of testing for seasonal efficiency of unitary air conditioners and heat pumps.*

[113] McMullan, J. T., Morgan, R. and Hughes, D. W. (1981). 'The discrepancy between heat pump field and test performance: a simulation study'. *Int. J. Energy Res.* **5** (1), 83–94.

[114] Joint AEIC-EEI heat pump committee (1948). 'Suggested field test procedure for determination of coefficient of performance and performance factor of an electric heat pump while operating on the heating cycle'. *Edison Electric Inst. Bull.* **16**, 341–8.

[115] Didion, D. A. (1979). 'New testing and rating procedures for seasonal performance of heat pumps'. *ASHRAE J.* **21** (9), 40.

[116] Institute of Refrigeration (1979). *Mechanical integrity of vapour compression refrigerating systems for plant and equipment supplied and used in the UK. Part 1: Design and construction of systems using ammonia as the refrigerant,* Wallington, Surrey, UK.

[117] Air Conditioning Industry Approvals Authority (1981). *Interim standard for rating and performance of air to air and air to water heat pumps up to 15 kW nominal output,* Millbank, London.

[118] Air Conditioning Industry Approvals Authority (1981). *Interim standard for safety of air to air and air to water heat pumps up to 15 kW nominal output,* Millbank, London.

# System design considerations

4

There are interactions between heat pumps and the systems in which they are used. Whatever type of heat pump is used in any application, it forms part of a larger system including both the heat source and the equipment using the heat produced. The design of the heat pump must be related to the system in which it is to be used and the incorporation of the heat pump may lead to modifications in the rest of the system. The more integrated the approach the better the chances of success.

In applications requiring large amounts of heat, such as industrial process heating and heat-recovery heating of large buildings, the heat pump specification is inevitably linked to the overall design. However, for space heating, whether for a school, warehouse, factory, shop, or house, heat pump equipment can be specified with little or no thought about the system it is serving. The suitability of heat pumps for specific domestic, commercial, and industrial applications is considered in the next chapters. In this chapter, general topics affecting heat pump system design are considered, including sources of heat, methods of storing heat, and the effect of heat pump systems on electricity supply. Factors affecting space-heating design in particular are then considered in some detail.

## 4.1 General considerations

### 4.1.1 Heat sources

Heat pumps may be classified according to their heat source. Ambient source heat pumps abstract heat from a source external to the process or building to which heat is supplied. Heat recovery devices use heat produced as a by-product of some other process, such as cooling. The more commonly advocated sources of heat for both classes of heat pump are considered below.

*Table 4.1* Air temperature drop (K) for a flow rate of 0.1 m³s⁻¹ for every kW
extracted

| Starting condition | | | |
|---|---|---|---|
| Dry bulb temperature (°C) | Wet bulb temperature, (°C) | Relative humidity, (%) | Temperature drop (K) |
| 10 | 5.6 | 50 | 8.0 |
| 5 | 1.5 | 50 | 7.7 |
| 0 | −3.0 | 50 | 7.5 |
| 5 | 5.0 | 100 | 4.2 |
| 0 | 0 | 100 | 4.7 |

(A) OUTDOOR AIR.   Outdoor air, because of its low density, has a low
heat capacity compared with liquids and solids. It is also subject to wide and
rapid variations in temperature and humidity. Despite these disadvantages,
it is the most widely used heat source for space-heating heat pumps, and its
unrestricted availability makes it the obvious choice for any type of heat
pump which is to serve a mass market. It is widely used for large numbers of
domestic installations in the US.

The energy required to move air across conventional heat exchangers is
usually less than one-twentieth of the heat energy which is extracted from
the air stream. In general, an air flow of around 0.1 m³ s⁻¹ is used for every
kilowatt of heat extracted, and the heat capacity of air is such that this
extraction rate is obtained with an air-temperature drop of between 4 and 8
K, depending on the temperature and humidity of the ambient air as shown
in Table 4.1. (As the behaviour of heat exchangers when wet is not fully
quantified it is usual to design for dry conditions and use the advantageous
heat transfer at high humidities to compensate for the equally unquantified
effects of frost formation.) With single-stage vapour compression refrigeration equipment, air-source heat pumps may be operated down to −15 to
−20°C, but their effectiveness is low at such temperatures and they are
seldom used on their own for heating applications where air temperatures
fall below about 2°C. The variations in c.o.p. with outside temperature for a
typical reversible air-source heat pump and for a projected heating-only unit
are shown in Fig. 4.1.

Both the efficiency and the reliability of air-source heat pumps are
reduced by the formation of frost on the outdoor heat exchanger. There are
well-proved methods of removing frost (see Section 3.9), but the requirements for effective defrosting with minimum energy use have provided
reliability problems which have not always been fully overcome. Less than
2% of the total energy is typically used for defrosting [1], but the decrease in

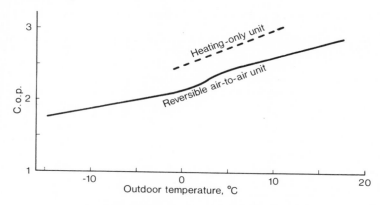

*Fig. 4.1* Performance of two air-source heat pumps.

performance due to build-up of frost before defrosting is uncertain [2], and may increase the effective frost penalty to between 5 and 10%.

(B) WATER.   Water is an excellent heat source where it is readily available in sufficient quantities which do not freeze in winter. Rivers, lakes, and ground water may be used as heat sources for small heat pumps (subject to local water authority approval and no legal obstacles) and these together with sea water may be considered for larger installations. There are a number of sea water source installations in use including an open-air swimming pool in East Friesland and a gas-engine driven unit heating a Marseilles theatre. The use of sea water as a source for small installations on ships or marine structures is an obvious but rather restricted application.

For all water sources, pumping power requirements to supply and dispose of the water must be fully assessed. Water authority requirements must be observed [3,4]. Particular care must be taken to ensure that an analysis of the water confirms the suitability of the proposed heat exchanger materials, to avoid possible corrosion problems. Subject to these requirements, the high thermal capacity of water and its good heat-transfer characteristics make it an attractive heat source. Temperature drops may be limited, particularly for river water in winter, but a flow of only 0.12 litre s$^{-1}$ with a temperature drop of 2 K will yield 1 kW, and the heat exchangers required are compact.

(C) GEOTHERMAL ENERGY.   Geothermal energy is occasionally proposed as a heat source. In regions where hot springs are found there may be sufficient heat available from the terrestrial flux, but away from such areas it is rare to find a flux in excess of 2 W m$^{-2}$. The average value on land has been quoted by Leardini as 0.063 W m$^{-2}$ [5]. As this is of the order of 0.1% of the heat loss from a normal dwelling there can be no prospect of collecting geothermal heat for individual houses. In areas where geothermal heat is stored in underground water, pumping may be worthwhile for larger scale district heating schemes, as is discussed further in Section 5.4.

(D) SOIL. Despite the low level of geothermal heat, the earth may be used as an effective medium from which to draw heat. Both the movement of ground water and the incident solar radiation heat up the surface layer of soil, and heat may be extracted from this layer by means of a heat pump. Sustainable extraction rates of $20-40$ W m$^{-2}$ have been reported, 25 W m$^{-2}$ being a common level [6–9]. The rate feasible is dependent on the composition of the local soil. Metal or plastic pipes are buried in the earth at a depth of 0.5 m or more, and brine, ethylene glycol solution, or occasionally refrigerants are circulated through them. During much of the winter the pipes may be embedded in a layer of ice which helps to maintain thermal contact with the soil.

An alternative method of collecting heat has been proposed in which instead of having horizontal pipes, a vertical 'U'-tube is installed [10]. Such systems are likely to be effective only for a short period unless there is considerable ground-water movement over the pipes, and a Danish study has found that vertical pipes run out of heat after three or four seasons [11].

The main advantages of soil as a heat source are its relatively steady temperature, the lack of any need to remove frost from heat exchanger surfaces, and the elimination of a potentially noisy fan. The reduction in soil temperature as a result of heat extraction has been determined by a number of experimenters, e.g. Rouvel [12], and is generally claimed to cause no problems as long as excessive extraction rates are avoided. The disadvantages are the need for sufficient ground area, the cost and the disturbance involved in laying the ground coil, and the difficulty of locating possible leaks after prolonged service. Assuming a heat pump c.o.p. of 3, an area of about 250 m$^2$ is necessary for the 10 kW heat output needed by a typical European house. Soil source heat pumps have not been generally used for reversible applications, as the drying out of soil on heating seriously reduces the thermal conductivity, making adequate summer heat rejection difficult.

Soil source heat pumps are popular in Sweden where over 2000 domestic installations exist [13–15]. There is also a particularly large installation in Meckenheim, Germany, where twelve kilometres of tube is laid over 16 000 square metres of ground to serve a gas-fired absorption unit [16]. Recent EEC studies in various European countries produce conflicting estimates of the economic viability of the soil as a heat source [17].

The heating performance of soil source heat pumps is claimed on occasions to be superior to that of air source units, due to the lack of fan energy use and the elimination of defrosting, but as all soil source installations are primarily designed for heating and most air source units are designed for cooling, this is to be expected. Given equipment designed for heating in both cases and given equal total costs including installation, there is likely to be very little difference in performance, and the air source unit has the advantage of being able to be proved prior to sale, whereas a soil source unit can only be fully tested after installation, a far less accurate means of evaluation.

(E) WASTE HEAT RECOVERY.   In any process in which cooling is used, heat is rejected which may be considered for use for local heating purposes. If the heat is rejected at a high enough temperature, it may be used directly, but if the heat-carrying medium is too cool for this, it may still be useful as a source for a heat pump. Waste heat from industrial processes may be useful at a higher temperature in the process, or may be used for space or water heating. Waste heat from milk coolers may be used to provide water heating for cleaning in dairies. Heat extracted from ice rinks may be used to heat adjacent sports halls and swimming pools. Even waste heat generated by decomposing dung has been recovered by a heat pump and put to good use [18]. In buildings, heat from air-conditioning systems and from lights may be used to heat exposed rooms in mild weather, heat from frozen-food storage rooms and cabinets may be recovered, and heat from exhaust ventilation air may be returned to the incoming air.

External waste heat sources are not common but are sometimes worth consideration. Water pumped out of mines and tunnels may provide a reliable heat source. An interesting internal-source heat pump system in a newspaper office in Liverpool uses water pumped from a tunnel under the River Mersey to provide cooling when needed [19]. Heat from sewers has been used, for example in a small heat pump at Nuffield College, Oxford. As sewage treatment depends on a certain amount of heat being present, widespread use of this source could be counter-productive if it meant adding heat at sewage treatment works. However, treated effluent from central purification plants is being used in at least one large (3 MW) Swedish district-heating, heat pump project [20]. Examples of many forms of waste-heat recovery using heat pumps will be found in Chapters 5–7.

### 4.1.2 *Heat storage*

Where heat is needed for an application in which demand is out of phase with the time of supply (for example, a process in which heating and cooling occur consecutively) the heat may be stored. Although it is possible to incorporate heat storage in industrial process applications, it is uncommon and heat storage is usually associated with space- and water-heating systems for buildings. Storage of hot water is normal practice in many types of water heaters to meet the rapidly fluctuating demands of users.

Heat pumps may be used in conjunction with heat storage in a variety of heating applications. In colder weather, the efficiency of an ambient source heat pump is reduced, or it may have insufficient capacity, and it may be preferable to supplement it with heat from storage rather than to use a larger heat pump [21, 22]. The stored heat may be provided by the heat pump at a time of reduced heat demand, or by an off-peak electric heater, or by a solar collector. Heating systems have been designed with storage on a daily, weekly, or seasonal basis, depending on the requirements. The advantages of heat storage (principally reduced running costs) must be balanced against the penalties of increased capital cost, bulk, and energy use.

In order to assess the value of heat storage in systems using heat pumps it is necessary to consider possible thermal storage materials. Physical properties of some storage materials are given in Table 4.2. The data given are indicative of the properties to be expected of the classes of materials, variations between particular products being expected. Data for soil in particular must be used with caution as there are very wide variations [23]. The choice of material in which thermal energy may be stored depends on the amount of energy to be stored and on the temperature at which it is to be provided. The commonest methods of storing sensible heat are in tanks of water for low temperatures and in specially developed heat-storage bricks for high temperatures.

For heat which can only be stored over a small temperature interval, materials with a latent heat associated with a change of state at an appropriate temperature may be considered. Such materials have not yet become

Table 4.2 Thermal storage materials

| Material | Melting point (°C) | Temperature range assumed (°C) | Heat storage | |
|---|---|---|---|---|
| | | | (kJkg$^{-1}$) | (MJ m$^{-3}$) |
| *Latent heat storage* | | | | |
| $H_2O$ | 0 | – | 333 | 333 |
| $NaF/H_2O$ | −3.5 | – | 323 | 309 |
| $KF.4H_2O$ | 18.5 | – | 231 | 336 |
| $CaCl.6H_2O$ | 29.2 | – | 712 | 258 |
| $Na_2HPO_4.12H_2O$ | 35.2 | – | 280 | 403 |
| *Sensible heat storage* | | | | |
| $H_2O$ | – | 90–40 | 209 | 209 |
| Soil: heavy, wet | – | 12–2 | 30 | 63 |
|     light, dry | – | 12–2 | 10 | 12 |
| Concrete | – | 25–20 | 4 | 8 |
| Cast iron alloy | – | 750–150 | 353 | 2428 |
| Fireclay bricks | – | 750–150 | 629 | 1309 |
| High density storage bricks | – | 750–150 | 553 | 2212 |

established other than in specialized aerospace applications despite considerable research and development efforts [24–28]. The principal problems are cost, heat extraction in the solid state, and long-term irreversibility of chemical or crystalline transitions. The latter is no problem in the case of water, and the use of ice/water storage for winter heating and summer cooling has been seen to have attractions in many countries [29–31]. Allowance has to be made for the 8% increase in volume on freezing, and ingenious methods including the floating off of slabs of ice from a submerged evaporator have been proposed [32]. Before the days of mechanical refrigeration, ice storage from winter to summer was common; but the economic feasibility of ice storage in conjunction with modern equipment has yet to be demonstrated.

As water is readily available in most places there is a danger of assuming that the cost of heat storage in water will be low. Although water storage is usually the least expensive form of thermal energy store, it is not necessarily cheap, a storage cost (including installation and insulation) of around £200/$m^3$ in 1977 being typical [33]. It is all too easy to take an irreversible decision to include water storage in a heating system before the costs have been determined and to end up with an uneconomic system. The full cost of storage tanks, thermal insulation, controls, and pipe-work must be assessed, as must standing heat losses, before the decision to use water storage is taken. If heat is stored at other than ambient temperature, thermal insulation of the store will be necessary. Physical properties of some insulation materials are given in Table 4.3. Knowledge of insulation and storage material costs and of energy costs will permit economically optimal

Table 4.3  Thermal insulation materials

| Material | Thermal conductivity $(Wm^{-1}K^{-1})$ for dry material at around 20°C |
|---|---|
| Opacified silica aerogel | 0.022 |
| Polyurethane foam | 0.02–0.03 |
| Expanded polystyrene } Glass fibre } Urea formaldehyde foam } | 0.03–0.04 |
| Mineral wool | 0.03–0.05 |
| Foamed glass | 0.05–0.06 |
| Vermiculite granules | 0.06–0.07 |
| Vermiculite board | 0.07–0.08 |
| Expanded clay blocks | 0.19 |
| Dry sand | 0.3 |
| Sandy loam (natural moisture content) | 0.5–1.2 |
| Heavy clay (wet) | 1.7 |

storage temperatures and insulation thicknesses to be calculated.

If heat is to be stored for a long period it is possible for a heat pump to provide summer cooling and winter heating by pumping heat energy to a store in summer and returning the same heat in winter. When this is done the normal definition of c.o.p. may need modification, and the term ACOP (annual c.o.p.) has been used to indicate the ratio of useful total heat output in both modes to total energy input. An example of this is considered in Chapter 5.

### 4.1.3 *Electricity supply*

The advantages of electric motors for driving vapour compression heat pumps have been discussed in Section 3.2. The convenience and reliability of electric motors should mean that they continue to be the main heat pump drives for all types of heat pump for the foreseeable future. This being the case, it is as well to be aware of some of the possible difficulties associated with the electrical characteristics of heat pumps.

For large commercial applications and for industrial applications there are no new problems. The characteristics of large electric motors, and the matching of load characteristics to tariffs are both familiar to the larger user of electricity. For smaller applications, and in particular for domestic applications in climates where winter heating is the main requirement, there are possible problems of starting current and load factor that may be less familiar to both designer and customer, and these are outlined below.

Heat pumps for domestic heating come in sizes from about 3 kW to about 30 kW thermal output, using electric motors needing from under 1 kW to 7 kW or more. Such motors are very much larger than motors used in any other domestic equipment, and in common with all such motors, draw a current for a short time on start-up which is four to six times the normal running current. This starting current may only last 100–200 ms, but can result in appreciable voltage drops and, as start-up is relatively frequent, can cause an unacceptable level of interference with neighbouring supplies [34]. The problem, which is more acute with single-phase electricity supplies than with three-phase supplies, can always be overcome by reinforcing the electricity supply (e.g. by increasing the diameter of the cables), but this is an added expense. In some countries, such as the UK, starting current liabilities could limit the size of directly started motors to a maximum input of about 1 kW. With this in mind, resistive soft starting systems have been devised which reduce the voltage dip of single-phase motors to less than one-third of that for directly started units so that in principle single-phase motors of up to 3 kW may be used. Above this level, three-phase motors would be normal [35]. Purchasers of single-phase heat pumps of over 1 kW input would be well advised to ensure that they have starting characteristics which are acceptable to the electricity supply authorities.

Load factor is a measure of the uniformity of a given electrical load over the year, conveniently stated as the proportion of the year for which the equipment would have to operate continuously at its design load to give its actual annual electricity consumption. Load factor is important, as domestic electricity tariffs are designed around assumed values of load factor for the total domestic electricity requirement. It is possible to design heat pump systems combined with fuel-fired heating in which the electricity requirement is very low in cold weather, giving a high load factor for the electricity use, and conversely it is possible to design systems with electric supplementary heating to have load factors much lower than is normal for domestic supplies. The effects of these different load factors on the electricity supply tariffs and on electricity supply authorities' attitudes to heat pump heating will vary, dependent on the overall load factors in the authority's area. The commercial viability of any supply authority depends on its obtaining appropriate relations between tariffs and load factors, and some sensitivity is to be expected in the consideration of heat pump equipment which may fall outside normal load-factor limits.

Electricity tariffs for commercial and industrial supplies in all countries, and for domestic supplies in some countries, include charges for maximum power demand as well as for electrical energy. Where such tariffs apply, particular attention to controls to minimize maximum demand is necessary. This may require integration of controls for heating, lighting, and other electrical services, in order to provide the most economic system over-all.

### 4.2 Space-heating systems

Heat pumps are at present more widely used and more widely considered for space heating than for any other application. In this application, they must compete with well-established equipment which will frequently have a lower capital cost. The appeal of heat pumps is entirely dependent on their potential for low energy use. It is not sufficient to regard the heat pump merely as a low running cost, high capital cost replacement for a boiler, with no further consideration of the heating system as a whole. In many climates the traditional US practice of regarding heat pumps as cooling units with a fortuitous heating capacity is equally inadequate. A higher level of design expertise is required than might be adequate for simpler heating systems. Some aspects of heating-system design including distribution of heat and effects of climate on design, which have particular relevance to heat pump systems, are considered below.

### 4.2.1  *Distribution of heat*

Traditionally heating systems distribute heat around buildings from a central heat source by using either air or water. Although in theory heat can be distributed by refrigerant pipework from a vapour compression heat pump, the practical difficulties of pressure-drops, lubricant return and cost are likely to prevent this, and heat pumps will continue to use either air ducts or water pipes to distribute the heat.

The heat emitters for air and water systems have different characteristics which must be considered when deciding which system is more suitable. Air can be distributed through relatively small outlets, but requires large supply ducts, and there is always the danger of excessive noise being produced by fans and/or outlets if insufficient care is taken in design. Water needs only small pipes, but requires large radiator surfaces which may take up excessive wall areas. The best arrangement might be to choose water and use it to heat large areas of floor or ceiling, but this is usually rather expensive and provides a heating system which is relatively unresponsive to controls. A combination of systems using water distribution and fan-blown emitters can give a high degree of controllability, particularly in localized areas. The choice depends on the designer's assessment of the relative importance of controllability, cost, quietness, and available space, based on his knowledge of how the particular building is likely to be used. The only effective way of keeping people cool in buildings is by keeping the air cool, so that if appreciable cooling is to be provided in addition to heating, air distribution is essential, at least within the heated or cooled space. This does not preclude the use of water distribution through the building as a whole, a good example being the closed-loop water source heat pump system described in Section 6.1.3.

Having decided whether to use air or water to distribute the heat from the heat pump, the temperature at which it should be circulated can be determined as an economic optimum. In a hot-water radiator system with a fuel-fired boiler there are no penalties in operating at as high a temperature as is considered safe; the higher the temperature, the smaller the radiator area required, and the lower the costs. With a heat pump it is different – c.o.p. falls as output temperature rises so that both cost and efficiency penalties are associated with increasing output temperatures, and balancing these against radiator costs will given an economic optimum temperature of 45–50°C, which is lower than the 80°C or so generally used with boiler-operated systems. Radiators for use at these lower temperatures will cost substantially more, as over twice the surface area will be needed. This is preferable to the increased capital and running costs of a heat pump designed to provide higher water temperatures. Similar arguments applied to air-distribution systems yield even lower optimum temperatures, as ductwork costs are related more to duct length than to air-handling capacity, so that marginal costs of increased air flow are low. The need for increased fan power partly balances this, giving typical optimum air distribution temperatures of around 35°C. These optima, it is emphasized, are economic and are not based on either technical or comfort requirements, both of which can be met over a wide range of distribution temperatures. The temperatures suggested above apply to new installations. If a heat pump is being selected as a replacement for an existing heater, some compromise on supply temperatures may be necessary.

For smaller premises such as shops and homes, there is the further choice between split and packaged heat pumps. Packaged units are single, self-contained units having the advantage of factory sealing and easy installation. Split units, in which the evaporator and condenser are in separate packages connected by refrigerant piping, offer greater flexibility of distribution system design as the indoor heat exchanger can be placed at any convenient point within the building. For larger buildings a similar choice exists between a central unit and separate units for separate zones.

Whatever the system installed, it is important that the heat being distributed is not lost. The author has found heat losses from ducts accounting for 20% of annual heating energy use in a domestic installation, and comparable figures in other installations may not be unusual. Adequate thermal insulation of pipes and ducts is straightforward, as is the calculation of heat losses from them for given levels of insulation, and these calculations are an essential part of the design process. Contrary to a common assumption, the lower than usual distribution temperatures associated with heat pump systems do not reduce the need for adequate pipe and duct insulation, and they make the recognition of insulation deficiencies less obvious once the system is in use.

### 4.2.2 *Effects of climate on heating-system design*

Winter climate has an important effect on heat pump design, particularly for air-source heat pumps prone to heat exchanger frosting. Defrosting requirements have been considered in Section 3.9. Climate also affects wider aspects of heating-system design. As far as heat pump space heating is concerned, climates may be classified into three broad types; (i) climates in which cooling is a necessity and heating needs are small by comparison, such as the southern US, (ii) climates in which cooling and heating are equally important, typically areas a long way from oceans, and (iii) climates in which heating is a major need and cooling is either seldom needed or not required at all, as in northern Europe.

In the first type of climate a heat pump is primarily a cooler, offering the bonus of economic winter heating for little additional capital cost. The main annual energy requirement is for cooling so that heating efficiency is relatively unimportant. The design of equipment of this type is well established in the US, and the systems into which it is incorporated follow normal air-conditioning practice.

In the second type of climate, summer to winter temperature swings can be very large (a 50°C temperature difference between summer and winter design conditions is quite possible), and winter temperatures may fall so low that the heat pump cannot be used. In these conditions, a supplementary heating system to meet the design heat loss is essential (see Section 4.2.6) so, as for the first type of climate, heat pumps designed and installed on the basis of cooling capacity requirements alone are quite suitable.

Heat pumps designed for the first two climates are not well suited to the third, where maximum heating efficiency is required. A heat pump is likely to have higher capital costs than a wide range of well established alternative heating systems, which must be offset by reduced running costs. Heat pumps designed well enough to meet these criteria of high heating efficiency and modest capital cost are slow to emerge – principal developments have taken place in Sweden, Germany, and the Netherlands, but there has been a growing awareness by US and Japanese manufacturers of the need for a heat pump suitable for this type of climate. The potential markets in northern Europe, Japan, northern US, and Canada which now exist as a result of the increase in world fuel prices in the early 1970s have yet to be exploited, and fierce international competition could well be a major feature of heat pump developments in the 1980s.

### 4.2.3 'Free' heat

'Free' heat is that energy which contributes to space heating, but is either purchased for some other purpose (such as lighting) or is not purchased at all (e.g. sunshine). It is particularly important to allow for free heat in heat pump heating systems, as without it both the energy savings and the heat pump size would be overestimated, with possibly serious economic consequences.

If energy is used to produce motion, light, or sound, there are inefficiencies in the process, and a proportion of the energy used is immediately emitted as heat. The remainder of the energy does the job which is required but, by the time the motor stops accelerating, the light is seen, or the sound is heard, this too is converted to heat, and the whole of the energy input is a heat input some of which has been temporarily used for another purpose. Thus, any appliance using 1 kW may be regarded as a 1 kW heater. If the energy used is purchased primarily for a non-heating purpose (as with lights, typewriters, or television sets) the heat emitted may be regarded as 'free' heat.

A second source of free heat is human (or animal) metabolism. The energy is extracted from chemical conversion of food and emitted to the air around the body by radiation, convection and exhalation. A further source of free heat is sunshine, either direct or diffuse, which enters all the glazed areas of buildings.

The combined effect of these three sources of free heat is to reduce the space-heating requirements of the building to an extent which depends on the temperature required, the amount of free heat, and the rate of heat loss from the building [36–38]. There is a relationship between the level of thermal insulation and the effect of free heat. The thermal capacity of the building also has an effect on the efficiency of free heat utilization, especially for solar heat which can be very variable in the short term. The extent of the thermal capacity effect is dependent on the building occupancy pattern and on the methods of heat emission and control. Typical daily energy contributions from various free-heat sources are listed in Table 4.4.

*Table 4.4* Typical daily 'free-heat' energy

| Building type | Source | Average daily 'free heat' (kWh) |
|---|---|---|
| House | People – family of 4, 1 at home all day | 3.5 |
| | Cooking – electric | 3.5 |
| | Lights – winter average in UK | 1.5 |
| | Television – approximately | 1 |
| | Water heating – 30% of energy use for family of 4 | 3 |
| | Sunshine – south-facing 86m$^2$ semi-detached house [39] | |
| | January | 4.8 |
| | March | 14.5 |
| | June | 31.8 |
| Office | People – 20 people for 8 h | 15 |
| | Lights – 20 W m$^{-2}$ over 150 m$^2$ for 10 h | 30 |
| | Sunshine – 10 m$^2$ south-facing single glazing in the UK in winter | 10–15 |
| | Machinery – small data-handling unit, 1 kW continuous | 24 |
| Shop | People – average 100 people for 8 h | 88 |
| | Lights – 20 Wm$^{-2}$ over 1000 m$^2$ for 10 h | 200 |
| | Frozen food display – 5 kW average | 120 |
| School-room | People – 30 children for 6 h | 13.5 |
| | Lights – 20 W m$^{-2}$ over 150 m$^2$ for 6 h | 18 |
| Factory | People – 50 people × 3 shifts, heavy work | 240 |
| | Machines – 50 h.p. continuous at 85% efficiency | 1060 |
| | Lights – 12 W m$^{-2}$ continuous over 1000 m$^2$ | 290 |

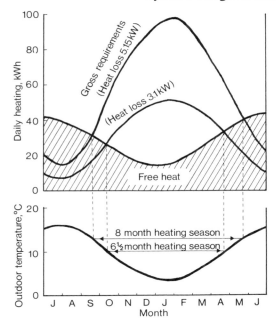

*Fig. 4.2* Free heat contribution to space heating. After Siviour [39].

The effect of free heat on annual heating energy use is seen in Fig. 4.2, in which the gross heat requirements of an 86 m² house are shown for two levels of thermal insulation. The figure is based on monthly averages and there will be considerable day-to-day variations in both heating requirement and solar free heat. The free heat from people, sunshine, and appliances supplies approximately 9000 kWh of the gross requirement of 21000 kWh in the less-well-insulated house, leaving 12000 kWh to be met by the heating system. The same free-heat sources provide approximately 7000 out of 11000 kWh in the better insulated house, reducing the heating system requirement to 4000 kWh. In addition to reducing the heating requirement, insulation has shortened the heating season from 8 months to $6\frac{1}{2}$ months.

A convenient, simple parameter to use to allow for free heat gains is the no-heating balance point, the outdoor temperature above which on average no heating is required. In the example above this is 13°C for the worse and 10°C for the better insulated house. Values are likely to lie between 10 and 16°C, a value of 13°C being typical for existing British housing. In well-insulated office buildings with low amounts of glazing, balance points below 0°C are possible, giving a very low heating requirement, but possibly an excessively long air-conditioning season. In shops, where free heat is dependent on a widely varying density of occupation, the no-heating balance point is less relevant, as anyone who has left shopping for Christmas presents until the last minute will readily appreciate.

### 4.2.4 *Comfort considerations*

Heat distribution temperatures are generally lower for heat pump heating systems than for boiler-operated systems, the reason being economic as explained previously. It is appropriate therefore to consider whether this will have any adverse effect on comfort levels within the heated space.

The comfort requirements of human beings have been very fully studied in recent years by Fanger, McIntyre, and others [40–43]. Equations have been derived, based on human responses to a wide range of conditions, which describe the interactions of radiant temperature, air temperature, air movement, humidity, clothing, and activity in relation to comfort. Comfort is principally determined by feelings of warmth, and it has been shown that warmth may be achieved as effectively with relatively low heating temperatures as with higher temperatures, as long as a correct balance between air temperature and radiant temperature is maintained. This means that comfortable conditions may be obtained with large, low temperature radiant heaters (whether floors, ceiling panels, or radiators) as well as with conventional radiators.

With warm-air distribution, warmth may be equally well obtained, but some care is necessary to obtain even distribution while avoiding draughts. The type of air movement which is subjectively considered draughty is not well defined, and air speeds above 0.15–0.25 m s$^{-1}$ (dependent on air temperature) may produce complaints. A speed of 0.15 m s$^{-1}$ at a temperature of 20°C appears to be an acceptable level of air movement.

In many countries, indoor humidity in summer can reach uncomfortable levels, and heating systems using reversible heat pumps can provide dehumidification and cooling more cheaply than full air-conditioning systems. This advantage of the heat pump may make it preferable to other heating systems, particularly in commercial buildings in countries with only an intermittent cooling requirement.

### 4.2.5 *Noise*

One specific aspect of comfort which has not been considered in the previous section is noise, which is simply unwanted sound. Compressors, pumps, and fans all generate noise. Results of measurements of sound pressure levels carried out at typical air-to-air domestic heat pump installations are illustrated in Fig. 4.3, demonstrating a frequency spectrum roughly corresponding to equal loudness over most of the range. As there are no

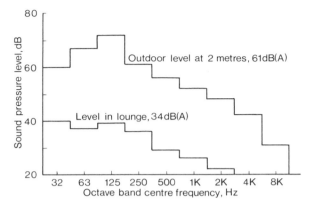

*Fig. 4.3* Sound pressure levels for typical air-to-air heat pump installations.

dominant frequencies, problems regarding the specific nature of the noise produced by such units are unlikely, only the overall level of noise need be a matter of concern.

Noise is usually expressed in terms of sound pressure level, in decibels relative to a level of $2 \times 10^{-5}$ N m$^{-2}$ and in order to give a measure corresponding to the sensation of noise, a weighted logarithmic average over the audible frequency range is calculated, using a standard weighting scale known as an A weighting, and giving a result expressed in dB(A). The averaging is automatically carried out on most noise measurement meters, giving a dB(A) reading directly. Criteria for acceptable noise levels in various environments may be found in systems application guides and noise control textbooks (e.g. [44, 45]). These are expressed in dB(A) or according to noise rating (NR) or noise criterion (NC) scales.

The NR and NC scales are favoured in Europe and in the US respectively, and the differences between them are small, as is seen in Fig. 4.4. The NR or NC level corresponds to the highest curve which the sound spectrum intersects at any frequency, and thus aims to measure the level of the most annoying frequency. This is fundamentally different from the dB(A) rating, which represents an average annoyance level over the whole spectrum. Nevertheless, over a fairly wide range of broad spectrum mechanically generated noises, the approximate relationship

$$dB(A) = NR + 6(\pm 2)$$

is found to be applicable so that, for example, a noise giving NR 30 would be likely to lie between 34 dB(A) and 38 dB(A). The NR criteria have been partially adopted by the International Standards Organisation (ISO), and this system is used below.

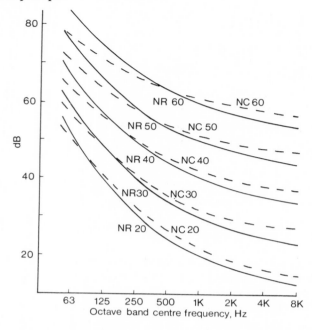

*Fig. 4.4* Octave band sound pressure level limits for NR and NC criteria.

Acceptable indoor noise levels depend on the sort of activity against which the noise is heard. Advisory criteria recommended by a number of sources [45, 46] are NR25 for bedrooms and NR 30 for living rooms in which people wish to sit quietly. In areas such as workrooms and garages, a level of up to NR45 would be acceptable. Levels for offices are between these latter two levels, depending on the type of activity.

Criteria for outdoor noise levels depend on the ambient noise level in the area, and on the distance from the noise source to areas likely to be occupied. A value of NR44 at a distance of 3 m from the noise generating unit has been recommended in the UK and the corresponding values at different distances may be obtained from Table 4.5, assuming a compact source and no reflections from adjoining buildings.

Noise from compressors may be minimized by the use of suitably designed resilient mountings and if necessary by the use of sound absorbing material in the enclosure in which they are mounted. Excessive pump and fan motor noise can be avoided by the use of efficient, properly balanced units. Fan impeller noise is mainly a function of tip speed, and may be reduced by the use of a larger impeller operating at a lower rate of rotation. Other sources of noise are reverberating or rattling metal panels, which can be avoided by

*Table 4.5* Noise ratings from a source giving NR44 at 3 m

| Distance from source (m) | 2 | 3 | 4 | 6 | 8 | 10 |
|---|---|---|---|---|---|---|
| Noise rating | NR47 | NR44 | NR41 | NR38 | NR35 | NR33 |

careful design and assembly, and air movement in ducts and flow control registers, the noise from which must be considered as part of the ductwork system design. Generally, noise is most likely to cause problems at a frequency around 250 Hz, and it has been suggested that adequate attention at this frequency should ensure satisfactory performance over the full range [47]. As the cost of making noisy equipment quieter is invariably greater than that of designing it sufficiently quiet in the first place, it is important that any heat pump specification should include agreed noise-level requirements. These may be specified by local building codes or regulations, or in the absence of these, the figures above combined with some knowledge of current practice in a particular application area will provide a guide.

### 4.2.6 *Supplementary heating*

The heat output of any conventional space-heating heat pump falls as the temperature falls. When outdoor air is the source, heat-source temperature and outdoor temperature are the same, and for soil, and to a lesser extent water sources, these temperatures are interdependent. This means that the heat output is least at the time when the heat requirement is most (Fig. 4.5), and there is some 'balance point' below which a heat pump fails to provide adequate heating. The example shown is for a typical British semi-detached

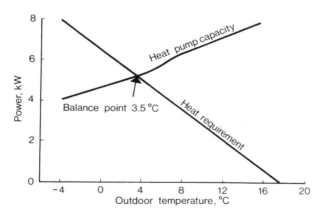

*Fig. 4.5* Heating requirement and heat pump capacity.

house of 86 m$^2$ floor area, with heat-loss characteristics typical of houses constructed in the 1960s and early 1970s. The basic principles are the same for larger buildings, including shops, offices, and schools, although the temperature above which heating is required will depend on occupancy levels, and may be considerably lower than for housing.

If the balance point is at or below the winter outdoor design temperature for the building, then there is sufficient heat output from the heat pump, but the amount of over-capacity at more typical heating season temperatures will mean long periods of short cycling leading to reduced efficiency and reliability, and a less steady temperature control in the house. This may in the future be overcome by the development of modulating compressors, but such equipment is not likely to be available for smaller installations for a considerable time. A heat pump sized to provide the full heating requirement will in any case be expensive.

It is normal practice to incorporate a low capital cost supplementary heating system and to size the heat pump for a balance point somewhere between the design heat requirement and the requirement on an average winter day. If the heat pump is reversible, the same effect is often obtained by sizing for the cooling condition and then taking the heating balance point as it comes. The supplementary heating can be provided by direct electric resistance heaters, but is occasionally from fuel-fired heaters, and could be from stored heat provided by off-peak electricity.

The amount of supplementary heating power may be relatively small as in Fig. 4.6 (a), or in climates with low winter temperatures may have to be equal to the full design heat loss as in Fig. 4.6(b). In this example the heat pump is switched off at temperatures below −12°C. The supplementary heating is in two 7 kW stages, both being used for temperatures below −10°C, only one stage being used between −10°C and +3.5°C, and the heat pump alone being used above 3.5°C. The use of multiple, discrete stages of supplementary heating is usual when a large supplementary heating power is used, availability of the stages being controlled by thermostats sensing outdoor temperature. A manual override for emergency use may be provided in addition.

For cases such as that shown in Fig. 4.6(a), the choice of size of heat pump must be made on economic grounds, and before this is possible, the relation between supplementary heating energy use and heat pump size must be determined. This is done from a knowledge of the climate and of the heating requirements (after deducting solar, appliance, and other free heat gains), and has been calculated for a typical British house with the results shown in Fig. 4.7. It is seen that in this case if a heat pump is sized to meet 64% of the house design heat loss (calculated as in the CIBS guide) it will only require 4% of the annual heating energy to be provided by supplementary heaters. If these supplementary heaters are direct electric elements, they will use

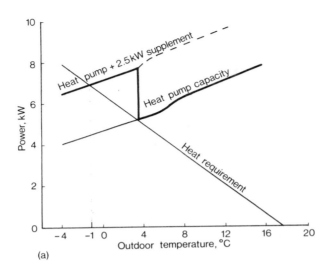

(a)

Fig. 4.6(a) Heat pump with single-stage supplementary heating.

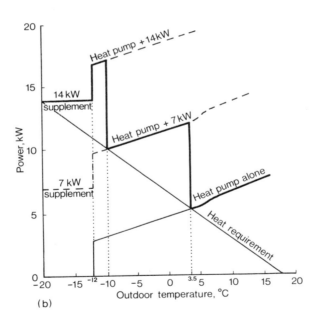

(b)

Fig. 4.6(b) Heat pump with two-stage supplementary heating to meet full design heat loss at −20°C.

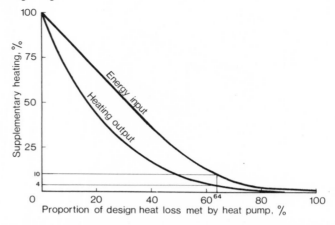

*Fig. 4.7* Annual supplementary heating output and energy input for direct electric supplementary heating in a typical British house.

10% of the annual electricity purchased for space heating. In Britain this represents a reasonable design target, larger amounts of direct electric supplementary heating representing high running costs for the owner and a poor load factor for the electricity supply industry [48].

There is, of course, no necessity for the supplementary heating to be placed within the heat pump package, and in some circumstances the design of the heat pump system for background heating only, with independent supplementary heating in the building may be advantageous. Fully automatic systems with large amounts of supplementary heat available can operate on supplementary heat alone in case of heat pump failure, and although this mode of operation may be an advantage from the point of view of comfort, it can have a serious effect on running costs if the heat pump is out of action for any length of time. Which system is best is dependent on winter design conditions and on the likely consequences of a loss of heating.

As an alternative to the use of supplementary heating, a heat pump may be run above the balance point but switched off and replaced by some other heating system at lower temperatures. If the other heating system is fuel-fired, this arrangement is known in Europe as dual fuel or 'bivalent' heating and in the US as a 'hybrid' system and such systems are receiving increasing attention. If winter design conditions are sufficiently severe, there will be long periods when the heat pump c.o.p. is low and a fuel-fired heating system is consequently more economical to run than the heat pump, and savings during these periods will compensate for the extra capital cost of providing two heating units, so the owner will benefit. The winter peak heating demand may be met by the fuel-fired system from locally stored supplies, so that neither fuel nor electricity supplier need be faced with high winter demands. Apart from capital costs, the overall feasibility of the bivalent system depends on the relative costs of electricity and other fuels and on the severity of the winter climate, and is at present most actively advocated in West Germany [49–51] where utilities give great attention to maintaining a uniform electricity demand. An example for the climate of Essen shows (Fig. 4.8) that a changeover temperature of 2°C requires a heat pump meeting 55% of the design heat loss, together with a fuel-fired boiler providing 50% of the annual heating energy. Both heat pump and boiler are operating near to their optimum efficiencies so that overall energy use is kept to a minimum. This means that such systems are particularly attractive to countries wishing to advocate national energy conservation, in order to reduce oil imports.

An alternative example for the climate of Croydon [52] shows that, at the same changeover temperature, the fuel-fired boiler provides only 36% of the annual energy and is less likely to justify its additional cost (Fig. 4.8). Even in such a climate, a bivalent system could be feasible if the heat pump is added to an existing fuel-fired heating system, the economics depending again on the relative prices of fuel and electricity. Heat emitters (whether hot water radiators or air ducts) would be sized for design heat requirements and for higher distribution temperatures than the heat pump could provide. This would give a distribution system with sufficient capacity for optimum heat pump distribution temperatures in the less severe weather when the heat pump would be used.

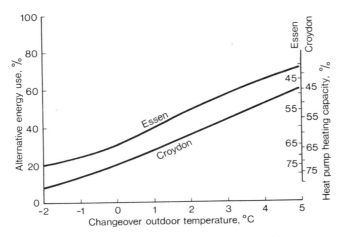

*Fig. 4.8* Alternative energy use, changeover temperature, and heat pump capacity at changeover temperature, for bivalent (alternative) heat pump operation at Croydon, England and at Essen, W. Germany.

Estimating the running costs for bivalent systems requires considerable care, as relatively small changes in heating standard, in free heat availability, or in actual changeover temperature can have large effects on the amount of fuel used. Calculations for any system should always be carried out for a range of possible conditions of use, if realistic running cost estimates are to be obtained [53].

## References

[1] Heap, R. D. (1977). 'American heat pumps in British houses'. *Elektrowärme Int.* **35** (A2), A77–A81

[2] Kelly, G. E. (1976). *Potential of air-to-air heat pumps for energy conservation in residential buildings.* National Bureau of Standards, Washington.

[3] Jänich, H. (1978). 'Erfahrungen mit Planung, Bau und Betrieb von Wärmepumpen, die als Wärmeträger Grundwasser nutzen' (Experience in the design, installation and operation of heat pumps using groundwater as source of heat). *Elektrowärme Int.* **36** (A2), A107–A110.

[4] Dybowski, M. (1978). 'Wasserrechtliehe Gesichtspunkte beim Einsatz von Wärmepumpen' (Impact of the Water Acts on the use of heat pumps). *Elektrowärme Int.* **36** (A2), A111–A113.

[5] Leardini, T. (1974). 'Geothermal power'. *Phil. Trans. R. Soc. London A* **276**, 507–26.

[6] Ambrose, E. R. (1966). *Heat pumps and electric heating.* Wiley, New York.

[7] Westh, O. G. (1977). *Heat pumps for space heating – results and conclusions.* Report No. 6, Teknologisk Instituts Forlag, Copenhagen.

[8] Schär, O. (1977). 'Die Anwendung der Wärmepumpe zur Heizung von Wohnbauten mit Wärmentnahme aus dem Erdreigh' (The use of the heat pump for heating dwellings with heat drawn from the soil). *Bull. Assoc. Suisse Elec.* **68** (4), 182–4.

[9] Saluja, S. N. and James, R. W. (1976). 'The ground as a heat pump'. *Refrigeration and Air conditioning* **79** (934), 38, 40.

[10] Goulburn, J.R. and Fearon, J. (1978). 'Deep ground coil evaporators for heat pumps'. *Applied Energy* **4**, 293–313.

[11] Fordsmand, M. and Eggers-Lura, A. (1980). 'A feasibility study on the improvement of the cop of a heat pump' (EUR 7048). In *New ways to save energy. Proceedings of EEC Seminar,* EEC, Brussels, p. 174.

[12] Rouvel, L. (1975). 'Soil temperatures following heat extraction by a heat pump'. *Heizung-Lüftung-Haustechnik* **26** (11), 393–6. (Translated as O.A. Trans. 2092, Electricity Council, London.)

[13] Mogensen, H. P. (1979). *The ground as a heat source for heat pumps performance and reactions.* Paper presented to XV International Congress of Refrigeration, Venice, Italy, September 1979.

[14] Lundin, S.E. (1980). 'The ground-heat source and heat store'. *Byggforskning* **4**, 4.

[15] Anon. (1979). *Nordic Symposium on Earth Heat Pump Systems,* Chalmers University of Technology, Earth Heat Pump Group, Gothenberg, Sweden.

[16] Field, A. (1982). 'Absorbing interest'. *J. Chart. Inst. Build. Services.* **4** (6), 55.

[17] Zegers, P. (ed.) (1981). *New ways to save energy, the community's energy R & D programme energy conservation* (EUR 7389 EN). Commission of the European Communities, Brussels.

[18] Eickenhorst, H. and Kimpenhaus, W. (1977). 'Agro-Wärmepumpe nutzt die Wärme von Stallmist' (Heat pump recovers heat from dung). *Elektrowärme Int.* **35** (A5), A290–A294.

[19] Liverpool Daily Post & Echo. *The mechanical and electrical services.* Information Sheet 2, Liverpool Daily Post & Echo, Liverpool, UK.

[20] Anon. (1981). 'Sewage is source for heat pump installation'. *Building Services and Environmental Engineer* **3** (8), 16.

[21] Neal, W. E. J. and Dodson, C. (1977). 'The use of solar energy, a heat pump and thermal store for domestic heating'. *Heating and Ventilating News* **20** (7), 64 – 6.

[22] Freund, P., Leach, S. J. and Seymour-Walker, K. (1976). *Heat pumps for use in buildings.* BRE current paper 19/76, Building Research Establishment, Watford, UK.

[23] Kemler, E. N. and Oglesby, S. (1950). *Heat pump applications.* Table 7.1. McGraw-Hill, New York.

[24] Anon. (1952). 'Chemical heat storage for heat pumps'. *Edison Electric Institute Bulletin.* **20** (May) 168–72.

[25] Shelpuk, B., Joy, P. and Crouthamel, M. (1977). *Technical and economic feasibility of thermal storage, final report.* C00/2591–76, RCA Advanced Technology Labs, Camden, NJ.

[26] Nemecek, J. J., Simmons, D. E. and Chubb, T. A. (1978). 'Demand sensitive energy storage in molten salts'. *Solar energy* **20** (3), 213–17.

[27] Humphries, W. R. and Griggs, E. I. (1977). *A design handbook for phase change thermal control and energy storage devices.* Technical paper NASA TP–1074, National Aeronautics and Space Administration, Washington DC.

[28] Gawran, K. and Schröder, J. (1977). 'Properties of some salt hydrates for latent heat storage'. *Int. J. Energy Res.* **1**, 351– 63.

[29] Kirn, H. (1976). 'Vermeidung von Netzlastspitzen bei Wärmepumpen-heizungen durch Einsatz thermischer Speicher' (Use of latent heat stores to avoid system peak loads from heat pumps). *Elektrowärme Int.* **34** (A2), A76–A78.

[30] Anon. (1977). 'Heat pumps'. *Building* **CCXXXII** (6970), 77.

[31] Matsushita Electric Industrial Co Ltd (1971). *Cooling and heating apparatus of heat storage type.* British Patent 1239997.

[32] Private communication from Professor P. V. Gilli concerning research at Institute of Thermal Power and Nuclear Engineering, Graz University of Technology, Austria.

[33] Ledermann, H. (1977). 'Space heating with heat pump and heat storage'. *Bull. Assoc. Suisse Elect.* **68** (4), 185–7. (Translated as O.A. Trans. 2161, 1977, Electricity Council, London.)

[34] Heap, R. D. and Blundell, C. J. (1977). *The use of heat pumps for domestic heating.* Paper presented at International Institute of Refrigeration, Commission E1, Belgrade, November 1977.

[35] Aubrey, D.R. (1980). *Resistive soft starting of single-phase domestic heat pump motors and its effect on starting voltage dip*, ECRC/R1297, The Electricity Council Research Centre, Chester, UK.

[36] Heap, R. D. (1978). 'Heat requirements and energy use in British houses'. *Energy and Buildings* **1**, No. 4, 347– 66.

[37] Siviour, J.B. (1976). *Designs for low energy houses.* ECRC/M922, Electricity Council Research Centre, Chester, UK.

[38] Wolf, R. (1974). *Chauffage et conditionnement électriques des locaux* (Electrical heating and conditioning of buildings). Eyrolles, Paris.

[39] Siviour, J. B. (1977). *Calculating solar heating and free heat and their contribution to space heating in dwellings*. Paper presented at CIB S17 meeting, Munich, September, 1977.

[40] Fanger, P. O. (1970). *Thermal comfort*. Danish Technical Press, Copenhagen.

[41] McIntyre, D. A. (1973). 'A guide to thermal comfort'. *Applied Ergonomics* **4** (2), 66–72.

[42] Humphreys, M. A. and Nicol, J. F. (1971). *Theoretical and practical aspects of thermal comfort*. BRS CP 14/71, Building Research Establishment, Watford, UK.

[43] McIntyre, D. A. (1980). *Indoor climate*. Applied Science Publishers Ltd, London.

[44] *IHVE Guide* (see bibliography.

[45] Woods, R. I. (Ed.) (1972). *Noise control in mechanical services*. Sound Research Laboratories Ltd, Colchester, UK.

[46] Anon. (1976). *UK workshop on heat pumps*. June/July 1976. Energy Technology Support Unit, Harwell, UK.

[47] Finkelstein, W. (1978). 'Ideal attenuation characteristics of sound attenuators for ventilation and air-conditioning plants'. *Heating and Air Conditioning J.* **48** (553), 26–35.

[48] Heap, R. D. (1976). 'Heat pumps for British houses?'. Section 3.19 of Courtney, R. G. (Ed.), *Energy conservation in the built environment* (see bibliography).

[49] Diedrich, H. (1976). 'Vermeidung von Netzlastspitzen bei Wärmepumpenheizungen durch Einsatz bivalenter Systeme' (Use of bivalent systems to avoid system peak loads from heat pump installations). *Elektrowärme Int.* **34** (A2), A71–A75.

[50] Eickenhorst, H. (1976). 'Wirtschaftlichkeit der Wärmepumpe' (Economy of the heat pump). *Elektrowärme Int.* **34** (A3), A136–A137.

[51] Kalischer, P. and Kebbekus, J. (1977). *Dual-energy heating. Fundamental considerations and practical experience*. Paper (3.1.2) presented at UNIPEDE 4th Electric Space Heating and Air Conditioning Conference, Bordeaux, October, 1977.

[52] Heap, R. D. (1978). 'Heating, cooling, and weather in Britain'. *Int. J. Energy Res.* **2** (1), 47–71.

[53] Heap, R. D. (1978). *Variability of energy use for domestic space heating*. ECRC/M1156, Electricity Council Research Centre, Chester, UK.

# Domestic heat pump applications

# 5

In any country, the first significant heat pump installations are usually not in houses, but in large commercial buildings, because it is in commercial or industrial applications that the largest energy savings from single heat pump installations will be made. Despite this fact, heat pump applications in the home are worthy of detailed consideration for two main reasons.

Heat pumps can have the greatest impact on national energy saving in the domestic sector, because there are many more houses than other types of buildings. On the assumptions made in one study [1] it has been estimated that savings of 7% could be made in the UK's energy budget by using heat pumps to provide all domestic heating, a figure which is difficult to match with any other energy-conservation strategy. (The same study estimated savings of approximately 4% from improved thermal insulation of houses.) Heat pump research and development for domestic applications is advocated in many countries, and is watched with interest by many more. Major reviews have been completed in Sweden, Denmark, and Ireland, there is active marketing in France and Germany, and increasing sales are forecast for the US, Japan, South America, and Australia [2–7]. Particularly in countries strongly dependent on imported oil, domestic heat pumps are likely to receive increasing government support in the form of either development finance or more obvious subsidies.

The domestic heat pump owner, unlike the commercial energy manager or the industrialist, is likely to understand very little of how his heat pump operates, so long as it does just that. His lack of technical interest and the limited mechanical engineering knowledge of house builders and architects, make the provision of suitable and reliable equipment a more onerous task for the heat pump designer. This task is not aided by the wide variety of possible domestic situations in which equipment may be installed. The domestic heat pump designer must have a greater understanding of the systems in which his equipment may be used (or misused) than the designer of larger heat pumps for commercial buildings where the responsibility for system design is shared with trained building services engineers. A useful check-list of relevant points for the potential purchaser to consider is provided, under 15 separate headings, in a recent Building Research Establishment publication [8].

In this chapter each of the possible domestic uses for heat pumps will be considered, including possible heat sources, design principles, and examples.

## 5.1  Space heating

### 5.1.1  *General considerations*

A heat pump may be considered simply as a competitor to other space-heating appliances, such as gas- or oil-fired boilers, warm-air furnaces, and off-peak or direct electric heaters. From a national viewpoint, we should also consider district heating schemes as competitors, either alone or in conjunction with electric power generation. For the householder with a satisfactory existing heating system, the costs and benefits of changing to a heat pump must be compared with the costs and benefits of improved house insulation and improved heating system controls, both of which also reduce his use of energy for heating.

In Britain, the cost of useful heating energy using domestic gas is around one third that of day-rate electricity. This means that electrically driven heat pumps need a c.o.p. approaching 3 if they are to compete in energy costs with gas-fired heating. Comparisons of capital costs depend on the heating power required, which in turn depends on the level of thermal insulation in the building. For houses of 80–90 m$^2$ floor area insulated to a heat loss of 4–$4\frac{1}{2}$ kW, suitably designed heat pumps could be competitive. At these and better insulation levels, heat pumps would also compete with district heating schemes, because the total heat load would be sufficiently dispersed for energy losses from heat distribution pipes to be substantial. In new housing, insulation to heat losses around 3 kW is possible, giving insulation against the British winter to such an extent that free heat supplies much of the need, and the additional space-heating energy requirements are very low, possibly less than the energy used for water heating. At this high level of insulation, the heating energy use may be insufficient for the running-cost savings from a heat pump to justify its capital cost. It seems unlikely, however, that such high levels of thermal insulation will be widely adopted, considering the present slow rate of improvement in Britain's low levels of house insulation.

The two main reasons for a householder to consider using a heat pump for space heating are a need for summer cooling, in which case a reversible heat pump provides both cooling and cheap heating, and a need to reduce heating energy costs. In the second case, the heat pump must be considered as part of an integrated package including thermal insulation of the building and the heat distribution system with its controls. Unless this is done, fair comparisons cannot be made between the heat pump system and other systems for energy economy. Some of the more important aspects of the overall systems design, including heat sources, distribution of heat, free heat, and supplementary heating, have been discussed in Chapter 4.

Air-source heat pumps for domestic heating are most widely used in their reversible form, capable of providing summer cooling as well as winter heating, and of necessity these use air distribution systems in the house. Such reversible heat pumps have a seasonal average c.o.p. of up to 2.5, although smaller units may be below 2, and as indicated in Fig. 4.1 on page 86 there is scope for improved heating performance. The effects of heat losses and of fan energy used to drive air through extended ductwork systems can, in practice, reduce the system effectiveness considerably, an overall c.o.p. of little more than 1 having been reported for some reversible installations [9, 10].

Although the vast majority of air-source heat pump installations are in the US (see Chapter 1), these are mostly in situations where cooling is the main need. Developments of air-to-air units designed for heating only in Great Britain are detailed below and air-to-water heat pumps are being widely developed in other European countries [11], mostly using outdoor air as the heat source.

In the US there has been increasing interest in using heat pumps in more northerly climates since about 1975 and the design possibilities have been intensively studied [12, 13]. Meanwhile in some areas of the country the proportion of new-housing heating systems using heat pumps now exceeds 80% [14].

In Britain the Electricity Council is in the process of assessing air-to-water heat pumps for houses. Thirty-one units selected from seven manufacturers (two of which are British) were installed in 1979–80 and about a further thirty-four were to be installed in 1982. Direct electric supplementary heating is provided by flow boilers. The assessment covers commissioning and installation as well as performance and reliability, and should provide the electricity supply industry with valuable background information when and if mass-produced domestic units become economically attractive.

The use of rivers and lakes as domestic heat sources is unusual as few houses are near enough to them to justify the piping and pumping costs. Ground water, extracted from wells near the house, is sometimes used [15–18]. Soil-source heat pumps, despite the apparent difficulties of installation and maintenance of the ground coil, are considered by some to be worth while because of the advantage of a relatively steady source temperature (see Section 4.1.1 D).

In houses which have mechanical ventilation systems, heat may be recovered from exhaust air and used to heat the incoming air, and this may be done with a heat exchanger, or a heat pump, or both. In such houses, the air distribution system including the fans may be provided as part of the ventilation system, so that the additional cost of incorporating a heat pump is reduced. As the heat source is always at indoor temperatures, there is no need for defrosting, and energy use can be low by comparison with ventilation systems without any heat recovery. These systems appear to be very popular in France but not in other countries where a need for mechanical ventilation has not been established. If heating combined with low natural ventilation levels is required in countries with moderate winter climates, these systems offer little if any energy saving advantage over heat pumps using outdoor air directly. In highly ventilated, well insulated homes, ventilation exhaust air plus compressor and fan input can meet the full heat requirement, but at lower ventilation or insulation levels, supplementary heating will be necessary in cold weather.

If some part of a house is to be kept cool (a cellar or a food store for example), then the air in this room may be used as a heat source for a heat pump, but this will not be sufficient to provide much in the way of space heating. Redistribution of heat in the house (e.g. from kitchen to living room) provides equally little energy, and will not form a complete heating system. Such internal sources, together with waste hot water from baths and basins, are of a scale which is more appropriate to possible sources for water-heating heat pumps which are considered later. The straightforward air-to-air heat pump is that most likely to be successful in most countries. Its use is best illustrated by performance data from an actual installation, which is presented in the next section.

### 5.1.2 *A straightforward air-to-air installation*

An American manufactured reversible air-to-air heat pump was installed at a house in the south of England in 1974. The performance of this unit was monitored in detail by the author over a 2-year period as part of the Electricity Council Research Centre's heat pump assessment programme [19]. The house was much larger and appreciably better insulated than average British houses, having a floor area of 235 m$^2$ and a design heat loss of 17.1 kW. The heat pump had a capacity of 68% of the design heat loss and direct electric supplementary heating was used. The total supplementary heater power was 18.4 kW, provided in two stages, a rather larger power rating than proved necessary.

The heat pump was mounted outdoors at the rear of the house (Fig. 5.1) and supplied a fully ducted air distribution system capable of providing heating or cooling to all rooms. Energy use was monitored on a half-hourly

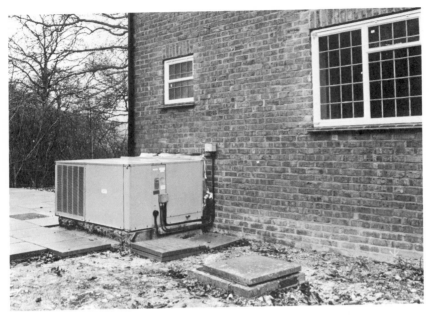

*Fig. 5.1* Heat pump installed at rear of house. Courtesy of Lennox Industries Ltd.

basis, using magnetic-tape recording meters, and was checked visually by weekly meter readings. Outdoor temperatures were monitored 3-hourly at a nearby meteorological station, and indoor temperatures were recorded continuously during three sample periods each of 1 month's duration. Operating time and number of defrost cycles were automatically totalled and the totals were noted weekly.

The overall energy balance for this installation over 12 months was determined, and the results are shown in detail in Table 5.1. The 12-month monitoring period experienced a temperature pattern close to the long-term average pattern for the area. The overall average energy use corresponded to an average power of 1.52 W m$^{-2}$ K$^{-1}$ including energy for lighting, water heating, and other domestic purposes, electricity being the only fuel available. The heat pump system required only 0.85 Wm$^{-2}$ K$^{-1}$, and 40% of the total electricity use was at lower cost night off-peak rates. Calculations making allowance for the heat gains from other electricity uses and from sunshine indicated an average heat pump c.o.p. of 2.5.

The number of defrost cycles (1379 in the year) was high, and a detailed analysis showed appreciable numbers of defrost operations at mean outdoor temperatures above 5°C (Fig. 5.2). As defrosting is most likely to be needed

Table 5.1 Monthly results for a domestic heat pump, 1975–76.

| Year | Period (day and month) | Time (h) | Compressor Use | | | | | Outdoor fan (kWh) (estimated)* | Supplementary heaters and indoor fan (kWh) (estimated)* | Heat pump system (kWh) | Other uses (kWh) | Total energy (kWh) | Mean outdoor temp. (°C) | Overall requirement (W °C⁻¹ m⁻²) assuming 18°C indoor temperature |
|---|---|---|---|---|---|---|---|---|---|---|---|---|---|---|
| | | | Heating (h) | Cooling (h) | Defrost (h) | Defrost (cycles) | kWh | | | | | | | |
| | 23.5 –27.6 | 848 | 75 | 4.25 | 0.59 | 34 | 334 | 53 | 113 | 510 | 1005 | 1515 | 13.7 | 1.8 |
| | 27.6 –25.7 | 672 | 5 | 0 | 0.02 | 1 | 21 | 3 | 5 | 29 | 899 | 928 | 16.5 | 3.9 |
| | 25.7 –29.8 | 832 | 0 | 0 | 0 | 0 | 0 | 0 | 0 | 0 | 420 | 420 | 16.6† | 3.8† |
| 1975 | 29.8 –29.9 | 753 | 74 | 0 | 0.31 | 21 | 338 | 50 | 61 | 449 | 978 | 1427 | 13.9 | 2.0 |
| | 29.9 –3.11 | 832 | 246 | 0 | 2.48 | 108 | 1040 | 165 | 269 | 1474 | 1175 | 2649 | 10.0 | 1.7 |
| | 3.11 –1.12 | 672 | 336 | 0 | 9.02 | 186 | 1292 | 225 | 487 | 2004 | 968 | 2972 | 6.1 | 1.6 |
| | 1.12 –29.12 | 672 | 409 | 0 | 13.04 | 239 | 1513 | 290 | 667 | 2470 | 1051 | 3521 | 3.9 | 1.6 |
| | 29.12 –2.2 | 840 | 415 | 0 | 10.10 | 236 | 1590 | 278 | 475 | 2343 | 1183 | 3526 | 5.7 | 1.5 |
| | 2.2 –1.3 | 677 | 297 | 0 | 8.67 | 170 | 1118 | 199 | 359 | 1676 | 1033 | 2709 | 4.7 | 1.3 |
| 1976 | 1.3 –29.3 | 666 | 395 | 0 | 9.24 | 225 | 1480 | 264 | 475 | 2219 | 1051 | 3270 | 4.4 | 1.5 |
| | 29.3 –26.4 | 672 | 211 | 0 | 3.13 | 112 | 869 | 141 | 221 | 1231 | 1157 | 2388 | 7.8 | 1.5 |
| | 26.4 –24.5 | 672 | 112 | 1.06 | 0.98 | 47 | 480 | 76 | 123 | 679 | 1098 | 1777 | 11.6 | 1.8 |
| 12-month total | 23.5.75–24.5.76 | 8808 | 2575 | 5.31 | 57.58 | 1379 | 10085 | 1744 | 3255 | 15084 | 12018 | 27102 | 9.4‡ | 1.52 |

* The sum of these two columns is measured, the split between them estimated from heating time.
† Occupied 2 weeks only.
‡ Over 49 weeks occupied period, 10.0°C over 52 weeks.

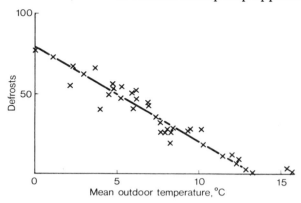

*Fig. 5.2* Weekly defrost frequency, 1975/76, for the monitored installation.

at temperatures close to freezing, this suggests the need for a more discriminating defrost control system to avoid unnecessary defrost cycles in the British climate. In addition to energy use and numbers of operations, maximum electrical demand in cold weather was studied. Relevant data for the coldest week of the 2-year monitoring period are presented in Table 5.2 and Fig. 5.3. As the heating system was used almost continuously during this week there was little use of the high-power supplementary heaters which could have adversely affected the electrical demand characteristics. Fan energy used was not separately monitored, but fan power was measured as 1.30 kW. The highest peak demands were recorded in milder weather when the heating system was used more intermittently.

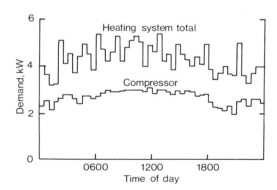

*Fig. 5.3* Weekly mean half hourly demand, week ending 3 February, 1976.

*Table 5.2* Energy use, maximum half hourly demand, and temperatures in a cold week.

| Date | Energy use (kWh) | | | Heating system maximum demand (kW) | Daily mean temperature (°C) |
|---|---|---|---|---|---|
| | Compressor | Auxiliary heaters and fans | Heat pump total | | |
| 28.1.76 (Wednesday) | 56.0 | 29.6 | 85.6 | 7.6 | −0.3 |
| 29.1.76 | 51.2 | 49.6 | 100.8 | 7.2 | +1.2 |
| 30.1.76 | 57.0 | 56.0 | 113.0 | 6.8 | −1.8 |
| 31.1.76 | 74.6 | 44.0 | 118.6 | 7.2 | −2.0 |
| 1.2.76 | 66.4 | 37.2 | 103.6 | 7.6 | −0.8 |
| 2.2.76 | 60.2 | 43.8 | 104.0 | 8.0 | −0.8 |
| 3.2.76 | 58.8 | 40.0 | 98.8 | 7.6 | −0.7 |

The overall conclusion was that the heat pump provided economical and effective heating in this installation, and the owner of the house was well pleased with it. However, when the house together with heat pump was passed to new owners, difficulties occurred which led to the subsequent removal of the heat pump. These difficulties may have been mainly of communication or may have been due to short-comings in the control of the whole heating system. They have been reported in a publication which includes several examples of successful heat pumps in homes in Britain [20].

### 5.1.3 *An experimental air-to-water installation*

The performance of a commercially available air-to-water heat pump of 4.4kW nominal output at 0°C ambient in an experimental house of 3.6 kW design heat loss has been reported in detail [21]. Although not typical of normal use the experimental house was provided with controlled heat inputs to simulate occupancy and was held at a constant 20°C indoor temperature. This enabled detailed and accurate performance measurements to be made over a period of several months.

, The heat pump provided domestic hot water as well as underfloor space heating. At design conditions hot water was delivered at 47°C and at a flow rate of 930 litres per hour. The overall c.o.p. was estimated as

$$2.11 + 0.042T$$

where $T$ was outside temperature in °C. For a typical heating season an overall figure of 2.3 would be expected. During intermittent use water heating alone was provided at a c.o.p. of 2.0 regardless of outside

*Table 5.3* Relation of running time to outside temperature in a BRE experimental installation. From Mountford and Freund [21].

| Outside air temperature, °C | Instantaneous heat output, kW | Run time, % | c.o.p. |
|---|---|---|---|
| −5.5 | 3.3 | 100 | 1.88 |
| −2.5 | 3.5 | 85 | 2.00 |
| +2.5 | 4.4 | 40 | 2.20 |
| +5.5 | 4.9 | 30 | 2.34 |
| +10.5 | 5.1 | 10 | 2.55 |

temperature.

Typical results taken from the published graphs show clearly how the running time varied with outside temperature (Table 5.3). These demonstrate that at average UK winter temperatures such a unit will only run for about 30% of the time.

### 5.1.4 *Small air-to-air heating-only units*

The design of small heat pumps for the UK market was studied by the author in some detail in the period up to 1979 and two prototype units were produced at the Electricity Council Research Centre [22, 23]. This design was intended to provide heating in a house of 4–4.5 kW design heat loss, with an annual energy consumption of 1800–3300 kWh per year depending on use. One prototype is illustrated in Fig. 5.4.

Calorimeter tests showed that the prototypes, which were not fully optimized, provided a performance in line with design predictions. Details are given in Table 5.4. To date there has been no commercial exploitation of this design, the basic parameters of which are as follows:

Compressor:          $22.3 \text{ cm}^3$ displacement hermetic refrigerating motor-compressor unit designed for refrigerant R22.

Refrigerant charge: 1.6 kg of R22.

Expansion device:   1.7 m × 1.63 mm bore capillary tube.

Heat exchangers:    three-row, 9.5 mm diameter copper tubes with continuous aluminium wavy fins at 1.8 mm pitch, 0.065 m deep.

Evaporator: $0.16 \text{ m}^2$ face area, $0.2 \text{ m}^3 \text{ s}^{-1}$ air flow at 90 Pa.

Condenser: $0.20 \text{ m}^2$ face area, $0.2 \text{ m}^3 \text{ s}^{-1}$ air flow at 80 Pa.

*Fig. 5.4* An ECRC prototype unit. The scale is 1m long. Courtesy of the Electricity Council Research Centre.

| | |
|---|---|
| Fans: | fully housed, nominal 1000 r.p.m. |
| | Outdoor fan: four-blade, 0.305 m diameter propellor fan. |
| | Indoor fan:  a double inlet centrifugal unit of 0.14 m inlet diameter and 0.18 m impeller length. |
| Defrosting: | 4.5 kW direct electric heaters embedded · in the evaporator. |

*Table 5.4* Performance of ECRC prototype unit.

| Parameter | Design value | Results of two tests | |
|---|---|---|---|
| Air to condenser, °C | 21 | 26 | 25.5 |
| Air to evaporator, °C | 5 | 16 | 11.5 |
| Output, kW | 3.21 | 3.7 | 3.2 |
| Compressor input, kW | 0.99 | 1.13 | 1.07 |
| Total input, kW | 1.13 | 1.29 | 1.23 |
| c.o.p. | 2.84 | 2.9 | 2.6 |
| Air-off temperature, °C | 35 | 41 | 39 |
| Evaporating temperature, °C | −6 | 8 | 5 |
| Condensing temperature, °C | 40.4 | 47 | 45 |

At about the same time as this unit was being developed a slightly smaller unit for single room use was designed for BRE [24]. This had an output of 1.8 kW at 5°C outdoor temperature and a c.o.p. of 2.14. Compared with the ECRC unit this has a smaller evaporator, lower air flow over the condenser, and a slightly higher air-delivery temperature. Appreciable effort was devoted to reducing noise in a series of three prototypes but as with the ECRC unit there has been no commercial exploitation of the design to date.

### 5.1.5 *Effects of cycling on performance*

The effects of on/off cycling of heat pumps on their overall seasonal performance have been the subject of a number of studies. One comparison of laboratory and field measurements on air-to-water heat pumps has shown improvements in the field of up to 20% over laboratory figures. This phenomenon has been investigated in detail and shown to be due to thermal inertia effects in the condenser and the heat distribution system [25].

With air-to-air systems this effect does not exist and several studies have shown that cycling can result in an appreciable loss of performance. One US study has shown a considerable reduction of performance of an air-to-air heat pump under frosting conditions [26].

In the Knoxville, Tennessee ACES project (see Section 5.3) a reversible heat pump was monitored in detail for comparison with an experimental system, and cycling losses were found to be important. For example, the mean space-heating c.o.p. in January 1979 was 1.65, but in milder weather the following April was only 1.42. Similar results were found in a monitored installation in the UK in 1976 [27] in which a combination of heating and cooling in mild weather (neither of which would have been required had a wider band of internal temperature been acceptable) together with unnecessary continuous indoor fan operation gave considerable wastage of energy. This particular installation had a maximum c.o.p. of 1.7 at 8°C outside temperature.

The use of more sophisticated system controls to prevent unnecessary use and to reduce the number of short on-cycles could easily be developed and would probably show greater energy savings than any other single heat pump design improvement. There is a widespread tendency to design heating systems as if the distribution system and the heat source are independent. For heat pump systems in particular this approach is quite inadequate if a good installation is to be achieved.

## 5.2  Heat pumps and solar heating

Heat extracted from rivers and streams, from the ground, and from air is all basically obtained from the sun. In this section, the 'solar' heating considered will be limited to those cases where energy is supplied from purpose-designed collectors of solar radiation which form part of an individual heating installation.

The combination of a heat pump and a solar collector in a space-heating system can have energy-saving advantages over either piece of equipment on its own, and general interest in such combinations is considerable [28, 29]. Using a solar collector as a heat source for a heat pump can remove the need for defrosting, increase heat pump output at low ambient temperatures, and reduce energy consumption. From the point of view of the solar heating system designer, adding a heat pump together with a heat store can serve two useful purposes. It provides a suitable form of auxiliary heating on days when solar collection is low, and it also enables the water supplied to the solar collector to be cooled, which improves the collection efficiency (Fig. 5.5). Looked at from either viewpoint, the use of purchased energy is reduced.

There are two basic combinations of heat pumps and solar heating. The first is the augmented heat pump in which all the heat supplied to the heating system passes through the heat pump. Heat from a solar collector is passed either directly to the heat pump, or else is stored to provide a source of heat for pumping when the ambient heat source is at a low temperature. With this arrangement the heat storage temperature can be low (water/ice latent heat is sometimes used), so that storage losses from even poorly insulated tanks need not be significant. Energy savings from 6% to 34% compared with conventional heat pumps have been claimed, the higher figures being associated with prohibitively expensive schemes.

As is seen in Fig. 4.1, p. 86, the change of heat pump c.o.p. with source temperature is not great, a 5 K increase in temperature giving only a 10% improvement in c.o.p., so that only modest reductions in energy use can be expected from solar augmented air source heat pumps. A 5 K rise in source

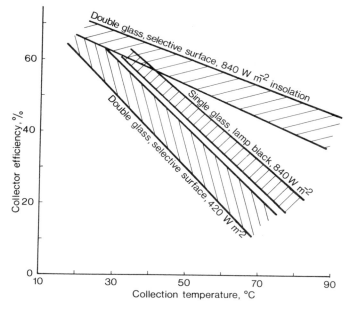

*Fig. 5.5* Efficiency of solar collectors.

temperature may need an amount of power as large as half the heat pump output, but only a small proportion of this power will be usefully collected by the heat pump. Most of the power used in raising the source temperature is wasted in the increased heat content of the air exhausted from the evaporator.

A simple air-heating solar collector in an augmented heat pump system was studied in the 1950s, showing energy savings of the order of 10% [30]. More complex systems with large water-storage tanks and large solar collectors were shown in a more recent analytical study [31] to use less energy than any other space-heating systems giving the same output, although capital costs were not considered. Minimum payback periods (see Chapter 8), of 37 years were found for similar systems in a comparable study, showing that the search for minimum energy use can lead far beyond the realms of economic viability. A Japanese simulation study [32] (with some experimental confirmation) showed that in a climate with a wide day-to-night temperature swing there were advantages in using solar-heated water as a night time source for a heat pump, outdoor air being used during the day. With such a system, the heat pump source temperature is on average higher than the outdoor air temperature, so there is a small improvement in performance.

Heat pump systems using water sources and able to provide either cooling or space heating together with water heating are available. These are generally used with a ground-water source, but they may be used with solar-heated water held in a storage tank. Water heating is provided by a desuperheating condenser coil, which operates whether the basic system is heating or cooling. One such combined system is shown in Fig. 5.6. Another interesting system using solar heat collected fortuitously by roof tiles to augment an air source heat pump supplying a large water store has been proposed in Britain [33]. Although air in a roof space may be heated during the day, it may also be cooled by radiation at night, so such a system requires thermal storage if it is to work effectively.

Another system which has been proposed uses a solar collector which is also the evaporator of a heat pump using R114. The condenser is immersed in a water-storage tank. Work carried out for NASA demonstrated a c.o.p. of over 3 at 27°C evaporating temperature for this system, but the practical difficulties of installing a refrigerant-filled solar collector would be considerable [34].

The second and most sensible combination of solar heating and heat pump is the use of a heat pump as part of a solar-heating system in which heat is only pumped when the solar-heat output is insufficient. Such schemes incorporate a thermal store in an arrangement such as that shown in Fig. 5.7, and at least one major heat pump manufacturer has produced a demonstration system of this type. The importance of these schemes may perhaps be judged from the fact that, in a survey of solar-heated buildings [35], seven out of thirty-eight incorporated a heat pump in the system. Systems of this type are more often considered in solar-heated houses designed for experimental studies than in solar-heated houses built for occupation. The experimental houses often have levels of thermal insulation which make the heating energy requirements very low indeed, combined with heating systems of remarkable complexity and expense. Such installations are valuable research tools, but cannot be regarded as models for future housing. Flexibility of use is assured in combined systems, but complexity results in heat losses from pipes, storage tanks and pumps which may take away much of the energy-saving benefits. Considerable design and installation care is required as in all solar collection systems to avoid the corrosion problems associated with mixed metals in recirculating water systems, and the capital cost of the heat pump is likely to be high compared with off-peak electric or fuel-fired auxiliary heaters.

One proposed experimental system, shown in Fig. 5.8, incorporates three heat pumps and three hot-water storage tanks, one for seasonal (summer to winter) storage, and one each for daily space heating and water heating needs [36]. Further complexities are added in the case of the Philips experimental house [37], in which waste water and the ground below the

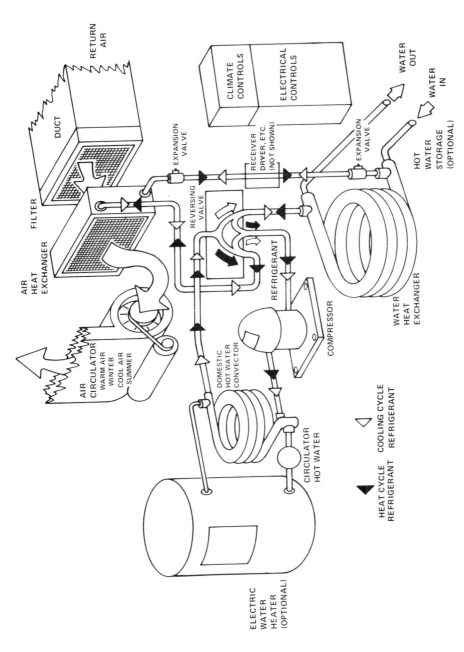

*Fig. 5.6* Combined heating, cooling, and water heating system. Courtesy of the Energy Conservation Division of Vaughn Corporation.

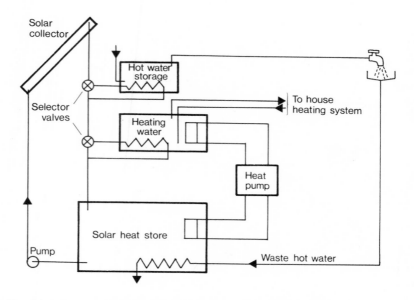

*Fig. 5.7* Solar heating system incorporating thermal storage and a heat pump.

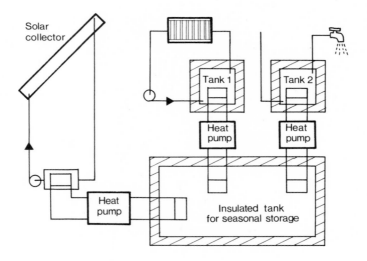

*Fig. 5.8* A proposed experimental heating system using solar heating and three heat
pumps [38].
Tank 1: storage for 1 day's heating
Tank 2: storage for 1 day's hot water

house are used as further heat sources. In this case, only 10% of the non-solar energy is provided from these further sources, showing them to be not worthwhile. Other solar houses using heat pumps have been reported in France [38] and Germany [39]. A Swiss manufacturer has offered a floor-heating system incorporating a solar collector, a ground-heat pick-up coil, and an ice/water heat store, claiming it to be competitive with oil heating despite a 50% higher capital cost [40].

A solar-heated house designed neither as a rigorous experiment nor as an economic proposition was the subject of a popular British television series in 1976. Practical trial of all manner of energy conservation devices demonstrated the superior economics of improved thermal insulation (i.e. reducing the heat requirement) over solar power and wind power, although the efficiency of the solar collection system was aided by use of a heat pump. Large-area conventional hot-water radiators running at very low temperatures provided good heating compatible with efficient heat pump operation [41].

All of these schemes lead to the consistent conclusion that, although the combination of heat pumps and solar energy can provide a given amount of heat at an energy cost which is unlikely to be bettered by other schemes, the combination is totally uneconomic [42, 43]. As heat pumps alone for space heating are generally only marginally economic (and that they are economical at all is not always agreed), and as solar space-heating systems can seldom be justified by accepted economic arguments, this conclusion about the combination cannot be surprising. Any potential application is limited in the amount of energy which can be saved, and the additional capital costs of a second energy-saving system give diminished returns. The best return on investment generally comes from the use, alone, of whichever is the better system for the particular application. The future of solar space heating must lie in the architectural approach of designing buildings which are well suited thermally to the climates in which they stand, and the future of space-heating heat pumps depends on their competitiveness in supplying the residual heating requirements of such designs, and the residual requirements of existing dwellings after they have been insulated to a reasonable standard.

### 5.3 Heat pumps and storage

Many of the solar systems described in the previous section incorporate thermal storage as well as a heat pump. It is of course possible to combine heat pumps with thermal storage in the absence of solar collection and some aspects of thermal storage have been discussed previously (Section 4.1.2). Such systems may be designed to store energy only when there is excess heat pump capacity, in which case long-term heat storage is necessary.

Alternatively the heat pump may meet a full day's requirement from a shorter operating period, such as an off-peak supply, and then a larger heat pump is needed. In either case there are considerable added costs to provide limited energy savings, as a number of studies have emphasized [44, 45]. If there is the attraction of very low off-peak running costs it is unlikely that heat pump heating will be able to compete with an all-storage, off-peak heater.

Perhaps the most thorough study of the use of a heat pump combined with long-term thermal storage is the Oak Ridge, Tennessee study of 'ACES' – the Annual Cycle Energy System. This uses seasonal storage in an ice bin together with a heat pump and a solar collector so that in winter both heating (to the house) and cooling (to the store) are used simultaneously. The stored cooling effect is used in summer. ACES is energy conservative to an extent which depends on a reasonable balance of annual heating and cooling requirements [46–48]. One particular type of system is illustrated in Fig. 5.9 and the basic concept is shown is Fig. 5.10.

Detailed performance data were obtained from an installation near

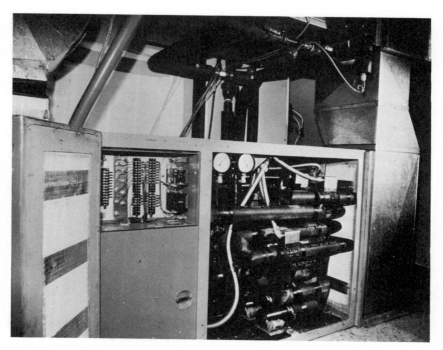

*Fig. 5.9* Heat pump mechanical package in an ACES installation. Courtesy of Oak Ridge National Laboratory.

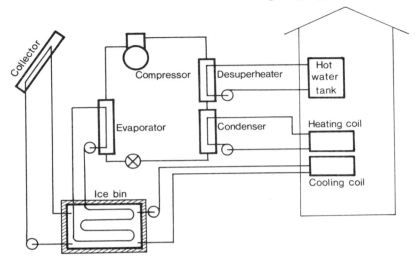

*Fig. 5.10* Brine chiller ACES system.

Knoxville, Tennessee, in which two nearly identical unoccupied houses were monitored in considerable detail. One had an ACES system, the other had a conventional heat pump system with two types of heat pump used in turn. Measured performance data are given in Table 5.5.

The study, on behalf of the US Department of Energy, included calculated annual c.o.p.s for 115 US cities, and detailed lifetime costing studies. ACES undoubtedly shows impressive energy savings but its cost is penalized by a high capital investment which is difficult to justify at present.

The low seasonal performance of the conventional heat pumps used as comparisons in this study suggests that investment of development resources in improved conventional heat pumps would be very worthwhile. In particular there is considerable scope for intelligent control of heat pump systems with energy saving in mind, and this development area is virtually unexplored.

## 5.4 Gas-fired domestic units

Heat pumps driven by gas engines and making use of exhaust heat recovery are in use in large commercial buildings and elsewhere, but the use of gas engines small enough to drive Rankine cycle heat pumps on a domestic scale is fraught with difficulties. Apart from cost, and noise, the maintenance requirement for small engines operating for perhaps 1500–2000 hours every year is considerable. Even automobile gas engines are not yet fully proven,

Table 5.5 ACES system performance [48].

| | ACES | 'ARI 2.46' heat pump |
|---|---|---|
| **Period December 1978 to September 1979** | | |
| Space-heating energy, kWh | 9125 | 9125 |
| Space-cooling energy, kWh | 5325 | 5328 |
| Hot water energy, kWh | 4392 | 3817 |
| Electrical input, kWh | 6719 | 12853 |
| 'ACOP' | 2.80 | 1.42 |
| | ACES | 'ARI 3.11' heat pump |
| **Period December 1979 to September 1980** | | |
| Space-heating energy, kWh | 9555 | 9525 |
| Space-cooling energy, kWh | 6292 | 6306 |
| Hot water energy, kWh | 3983 | 3769 |
| Electrical input, kWh | 6447 | 11358 |
| 'ACOP' | 3.08 | 1.73 |
| | ACES | Heat pump |
| **Peak demands (kW)** | | |
| Winter hourly | 3.3 | 12.0 |
| Summer air conditioning, hourly | 0.6 | 4.1 |
| Summer hot water, hourly | 2.8 | 4.5 |
| **Heat pumps performance** | | |
| ARI c.o.p. rating at 8.3°C | 2.46 | 3.11 |
| Heating seasonal performance factor | 1.58 | 1.99 |
| Cooling seasonal performance factor | 1.64 | 2.27 |

and these are larger and have much shorter running hours. The chances of conventional domestic engine driven units finding a large enough market to give low enough manufacturing costs to be commercially successful must be rather slim.

If an engine-driven, gas-fired heat pump is to be developed for domestic use there are attractions in using a Rankine-cycle, vapour-driven engine. Such an engine can be small and can have very low maintenance requirements. A prototype unit using a high-speed miniature turbine directly connected to a high-speed rotary compressor, was partially developed by Glynwed in the UK [49].

The turbo-compressor rotor of this machine was only 25 mm in diameter and designed to operate at speeds up to 150 000 r.p.m.; the basic operating

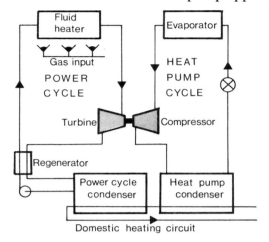

*Fig. 5.11* Directly fired domestic heat pump cycle.

cycle is shown in Fig. 5.11. The power-cycle condenser together with the heat pump had a total design output of 10 kW, equivalent to 1.17 times the fuel-energy input. This concept depends on the choice of a working fluid which is suitable for both the power cycle and the heat pump cycle, thus overcoming problems of rotating seals, and on the development of suitable high-speed bearings to operate in this environment. A low-pressure, high-temperature refrigerant with good high-temperature stability such as R114 is required. This imaginative but complex project was terminated in 1982 due to commercial changes and ongoing technical problems.

Gas-fired absorption units are being actively developed in countries such as the UK and West Germany where there is an established market for central-heating systems with hot-water distribution and where there is no need for domestic air-conditioning. These will provide space and water heating and will be sized as replacements for existing fuel-fired boilers [50, 51].

In the UK at least two groups are working on air-to-water absorption machines of about 10 kW output, with a target c.o.p. of around 1.2. Such units could be available by 1985 and they show a clear fuel saving advantage over gas boilers.

The German market requires rather larger machines and at least two companies now offer ammonia/water machines in the 20–40 kW range. In the US one manufacturer has a 15 kW air-to-water unit at a field-testing stage and two separate developments incorporating Stirling engines could be available by the mid 1980s. In Japan a 98 cc, two-stroke engine-driven, vapour compression system is being developed.

There are predictions of very large sales of domestic gas-fired heat pumps in the future, generally from commercially biased sources. While the absorption unit providing heating only is technically viable, its advantages over advanced condensing boilers are small and its added cost could be high, so its potential market share is uncertain.

## 5.5  Applications in larger residential units

Heat pumps are being considered for district heating in a number of projects in Europe and the US. There are two basic ways in which this may be done. A central heat pump may distribute heat to separate dwellings (a 'centralized' system) or a heat source may be distributed to the dwellings each of which has its own heat pump ( a 'distributed' system).

The distributed system is expensive in heat pumps but provides local control and metering and reduced distribution losses; it has much in common with the closed loop water source system in individual large commercial buildings. The centralized system is that most frequently advocated despite high distribution costs in both capital and energy terms.

A combined system with a central heat source upgraded partially before distribution could be attractive in energy terms but would be expensive in capital. If the dwellings are flats or apartments, a distributed approach to space heating can be combined with an integrated approach to mechanical ventilation possibly with heat recovery. Examples of this type of arrangement, together with details of a possible scheme using a heat pump with thermal storage, have been described by Mills [52]. Lower overall costs are obtained than would be possible with more conventional heating systems.

If a centralized scheme for a group of dwellings is to be considered, then there are additional opportunities. There are advantages in being able to use larger and more efficient plant with proper engineering supervision, which may make combined heat and power stations, fuel-fired heat pumps, or both together worth detailed assessment, and sources other than air become feasible. Current projects include a Swiss proposal to use power station waste heat with heat pumps to heat 1500 apartments and two schools in Birsfelden [53], and a European project which has highlighted the advantages of waste water from sewers as a large-scale heat source [54]. In the US a Department of Energy study entitled 'Heat pump centered integrated community energy systems' is hoped to provide a demonstration project by late 1983 [55].

A German air-to-water installation in 56 apartments using 65 heat pumps is the subject of EEC research [56]. In this case the high investment cost of a floor-heating system has made the overall project uneconomic compared with conventional oil-fired heating despite an energy saving of 30%.

The combination of heat pump and solar heating for a group of 12 well-insulated houses in the UK has been reported in which there were considerable practical difficulties [57]. Such combinations may provide energy savings if properly designed and installed but the effort and cost required to achieve this does not appear to be commercially justifiable.

Heat pumps for the heating and cooling of buildings using sea water as a source have been considered feasible in a number of countries, and in one case an experimental unit of 140–220 kW capacity has been proposed [58]. River water is also a copious source of heat, a potential capacity of 1000 MW being quoted for one case [59], and the economics have been regarded favourably in Germany for a relatively small 124-residence scheme. In areas with a suitable geological structure, geothermal heat is pumped to and from wells using a heat pump to extract additional heat [60, 61]. In one such scheme at Creil, France, 4000 dwellings are to be heated by a geothermal water source, in which the heat extracted is to be increased from 40 to 66% of the total heating requirement by use of a heat pump.

An unusual approach to group heating exists in Sweden where 88 detached houses with heat pumps use a common ground-source coil consisting of 33 km of 40 mm diameter plastic tubing at 0.8 m depth and 1–1.5 m spacing. The coil covers an area nearly equal to three times the floor area of the houses [62].

When a number of dwellings are to be served by a single heating system, the increased unit size means a fuel-fired heat pump is more likely to be worth while. There are a number of pilot schemes using gas or diesel motor drives either under consideration or in operation in Europe.

One EEC supported feasibility study in Germany examined the use of a coke-oven, gas-engine-driven scheme for 64 apartments [63]. This was an air-to-water unit with a 465 kW output at −12°C ambient temperature. The estimated payback time was 8 years. A study of a similar scale unit in the Netherlands used a groundwater heat source in a bivalent scheme for 45 dwellings [64].

In Switzerland, a gas-engine-driven system at Luzern provides 800 kW of heat to 62 apartments [65]. The heat distribution system here is of particular interest, in that some apartments are heated by relatively hot water using radiators, whereas others use the cooler water returning from these radiators in floor-heating pipes.

In Northern Europe, there is more interest in diesel-driven heat pumps, and a theoretical Danish study advocates these for district heating schemes supplying 2000–20 000 inhabitants [66, 67]. In Sweden, a pilot scheme supplies 55 houses with heat, and uses a turbocharged 9.6 litre diesel engine to drive a two-stage air-source heat pump. In this two-stage cycle, the first stage condenser is part of the second stage evaporator. This, together with engine and exhaust heat recovery, allows water to be supplied at 60°C with a first-stage evaporation temperature of $-20°C$. The turbocharger provides a more compact engine with a reduced noise level. Projects such as this will give useful indications of the reliability and maintenance costs of diesel engines as heat pump drives.

The problems associated with the use of heat pumps for district or group heating are basically those of the heating scheme, not those of the heat pump.

Costs of heat transport have been derived for district heating schemes [68], and levels of heat loss from distribution mains have been assessed [69]. The relations between fuel costs, load densities and pipework costs are not regarded as favourable in Britain at the present time [70], and future feasibility depends both on fuel-cost changes and on the effect of reduced load densities due to improved thermal insulation in houses. In any centralized system energy losses due to distribution will be high and estimation of peak demand will be difficult [71]. The larger the total heating load, the greater the distance over which heat may be economically transported. There is also evidence that energy use in unmetered collective schemes is at least one-third higher than in individual houses [72]. Such factors mitigate heavily against the energy-saving claims made for collective heating schemes, whether or not they incorporate heat pumps.

The thermodynamic principles of heat distribution have been well reviewed by Lorentzen [73] but combining these with the realities of costs and occupier habits is a complex task with many uncertain factors. Only large demonstration projects can provide authoritative answers.

Apart from economic feasibility, the main problems are finding suitable methods of metering heat, avoiding noise or (in air systems) odours being spread between dwelling units, and the difficulty of assessing the overall heat load after allowance for diversity and for free heat. If these problems are considered solvable, then the additional cost of including heat pump options in the original feasibility studies of any group or district heating scheme must be worthwhile.

## 5.6  Applications other than space heating

### 5.6.1  *Water heating*

The use of heat pumps for domestic hot-water supply was investigated in the US in the early 1950s, and trials of combined dehumidifiers and water heaters were reported in 1962 [74], but this application did not find wide acceptance. More recent studies have shown that using a heat pump to pre-heat hot water supplies could be economic by comparison with electric water heating [75], but this conclusion only holds where there is no off-peak electric tariff or other low-cost energy source which may be used for water heating. Serious interest in this application of heat pumps has arisen with increasing fuel costs or with the increasing relative importance of water-heating energy use in low-heat-loss housing. The typical UK household uses 10 kWh per day for water heating [76].

If pre-heating alone is required, output temperatures need be no higher than for space-heating heat pumps, but for a full hot-water service, units designed for higher-boiling-point refrigerants such as R114 may be more efficient than those using the more common refrigerants R12 and R22. A heat pump water heater may use an ambient heat source (air or possibly water), or may use heat recovered from mechanical ventilation systems, giving useful heat recovery at times of the year when neither space heating nor space cooling are required. Recovery of heat from bath and other waste hot water has also been proposed [77]. In all these cases, possible savings in energy costs resulting from the anticipated c.o.p. of 2–2.5 are small relative to the likely capital and installation costs involved.

Water heating may be obtained as a by-product of a heat pump used primarily for space heating, at a small additional capital cost. In this case, a water-heating heat pump condenser may be placed in series with the space-heating heat pump condenser, or may be in parallel and used either simultaneously or alternatively. Series connection enables the high temperature heat in superheated refrigerant vapour to provide water at a temperature of 50°C or more in limited quantities [33]. Using refrigerant 22, 10–15% of the total available heat may be available in high temperature refrigerant vapour, but with R12 and R502 little more than 5% will be available in a normal space-heating heat pump, and this may be insufficient to meet an adequate proportion of the water-heating requirement. Parallel connection makes the provision of hot water possible at times when space heating is not required, but this involves added complexity and cost.

Water heating may also be combined with space cooling, the economic feasibility depending on the duration of the annual cooling requirement. If the heat pump is designed for reversible operation, water heating may be provided from refrigerant superheat on both heating and cooling cycles, as in the example shown in Fig. 5.6, but there will always be days when the water heating requirement is not matched to the superheat available and a supplementary water heater is needed. Small units providing local cooling for cellars or food stores and pumping heat into domestic hot water were marketed in the UK in the 1950s, but sales were never substantial [78]. Desuperheaters for either heat pumps or air conditioners have recently been introduced in the US by three manufacturers [79], which are claimed to offer almost free water heating in summer when space cooling is required (apart from the $400 capital cost), and to reduce total domestic electricity demand in houses otherwise using direct electric water heaters. The claims made are realistic and such equipment is attractive to electricity supply utility and customer alike in climates with a summer peak load.

Further work on heat pump water heaters took place in both the US and Europe in the late 1970s, and feasibility studies showed that air-source water-heating heat pumps were much more economically worthwhile than solar systems which were in use. Payback periods of 2 to 3 years were anticipated [80, 81]. Units with an integral hot-water storage tank and immersed condenser, using ambient air as a source, are now available in the US at about $1000 installed [82]. On the basis of the American studies, a c.o.p. of about 2.5 is feasible for supply-water temperatures a little below summer ambient-air temperature, and this value applies if the unit is used indoors in summer to provide limited cooling of indoor air. An indoor source unit in winter extracts heat which must be replaced by the heating system, and an outdoor source in winter will give a much reduced performance. An overall annual c.o.p. of 1.5–2 could thus be typical.

The combination of limited capacity water heating with cooling is worthwhile and likely to become more common, although some equipment manufacturers are guilty of excessive optimism in their performance claims (the author has seen c.o.p. claim of 21!). The use of heat pumps to provide water heating in the absence of a cooling need can have little economic attraction at present levels of energy prices.

### 5.6.2 *Dehumidification and drying*

In damp, hot climates, dehumidification of the air is as important as cooling in providing comfortable conditions, and a certain amount of dehumidifying capacity is provided by any space-cooling equipment. Dehumidification is also useful in cold, damp conditions, and is then required as a substitute for, or an addition to, heating. Moisture is generated in houses by clothes drying, cooking, combustion of hydrocarbon fuels, all types of washing activities, and respiration. If it is not removed the humidity level rises until condensation occurs on the colder surfaces in the house, leading to problems of fungal attack and mould growth. Humidity levels may be kept down by a combination of heating and ventilation, and this is usually effective, but if high levels of heating and ventilation are maintained, the energy lost in exhaust air may be considerable. Lower levels of ventilation and heating may be ineffective in controlling moisture if the outdoor air is humid, as is usually the case in maritime climates in winter and, in these conditions, the heat pump dehumidifier may be used to advantage [83].

In the heat pump dehumidifier of the type which may be used in houses (Fig. 5.12), there is a single air stream which is blown by a fan, first over an evaporator coil and then over a condenser. Moisture is condensed on the evaporator and gives up its latent heat, and the cooled air is reheated at the condenser. The condensed moisture drains from the evaporator and is collected. The device operates overall as a heater, adding the compressor

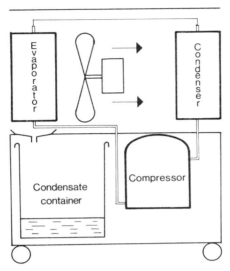

*Fig. 5.12* Layout of a domestic heat pump dehumidifier.

and fan power inputs to the heat extracted from the incoming air. In energy terms the moisture extraction is provided at no cost as long as the heating effect is required. Small units are available, with moisture extraction characteristics such as those shown in Fig. 5.13, and with power inputs of 200–300 W [84]. They may be used in cooler areas of houses such as passageways, or in cold store rooms to prevent condensation problems, but are not at present designed to be quiet enough for general use in living areas. Similar devices are used to help to dry out newly constructed dwellings.

The performance of a heat pump dehumidifier may be improved by incorporating a heat exchange system between the incoming air stream and the cooler air after the evaporator. In a larger unit this could be a simple runaround coil and in small units a counterflow air-to-air heat exchanger may be used. Such systems, sometimes known as 'geared' dehumidifiers, offer a doubling of effectiveness over the type of unit shown in Fig. 5.12 [85, 86], as is shown by performance graphs in Fig. 5.13. On the larger scale the principle may equally be applied to systems for swimming-pool halls.

As much of the moisture generated in houses is attributable to clothes drying, the combination of a heat pump dehumidifier and clothes dryer has attractions. Clothing may be hung in a compact cabinet and air circulated through the dehumidifier and through the cabinet in a closed circuit. Improved efficiency may be obtained by mixing chilled air from the evaporator with saturated air from the cabinet before passing it across the condenser – this reduces the condensing temperature and thus improves the

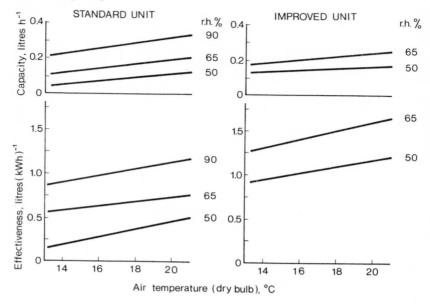

*Fig. 5.13* Performance of standard and improved small heat pump dehumidifier units, after Blundell [85].

c.o.p. Water is either drained away or collected in a container for later removal and drying rates are rapid. If the cabinet is left open the same unit may be used for general dehumidification of the air. Such a unit was developed in Britain, but to date the development has only had very limited commercial exploitation [87].

### 5.6.3 *Food storage*

Heat from enclosed food-storage cabinets (refrigerators and freezers) has from time to time been suggested as a possible energy source for heat pumping to provide space or water heating. (The Ferranti Fridge Heater, which acted as a combined larder cooler and water heater, has been mentioned previously (see Section 1.3).) The quantity of energy involved is small. Steady heat flow into a domestic freezer in typical conditions is around 100 W so that, with a typical cooling c.o.p. of 1, giving a heating c.o.p. of 2, the total heating power available is only 200 W. Although this may be doubled if the freezer operates continuously, either when air temperatures are high or during food freezing, it is still small compared with space-heating requirements. Even for water heating a supplementary system would be required although a good proportion of the average water-heating requirements, of around 400 W in the UK, could be met.

In food-storage equipment, reliability is the most important factor, and factory-sealed refrigerator and freezer refrigeration systems have been developed to a very high standard of reliability. To combine such factory units with water heaters, using on-site pipework and interconnections, would reduce this level of reliability. An effective system would require provision of adequate cooling capacity even when no hot water was required and could well extend the range of condensing temperatures above that for existing freezers.

It seems unlikely that the possible loss of reliability and the added complexity could ever be justified by the small energy savings involved. Only where domestic food is to be stored in a separate storage cellar or other large room can a heat pump be considered, where the need is effectively for space cooling or dehumidification.

### 5.6.4 *Domestic swimming pools*

Heat pumps may be used in swimming-pool applications for heating pool water and for dehumidifying air in the pool hall. Although private domestic swimming pools are generally considered as signs of rare affluence, the numbers involved in some countries (notably in Europe, West Germany) are sufficient for a heat pump industry serving them to have emerged. Pool owners are likely to have no shortage of funds, and pool heating can use a lot of energy, so that investment in heat pumping to reduce future energy costs is likely to be attractive. Pool water temperatures are low enough for a high c.o.p. to be expected.

Outdoor swimming pools may have their water heated by heat pumps using outdoor air as the heat source, but as in most countries the need for pool heating coincides with high levels of sunshine, solar heating schemes using simple collectors (which are quite adequate for the relatively low water temperatures required) are likely to be more attractive.

Indoor swimming pools not only require the pool water to be heated, but there is also a need to keep down the pool-hall humidity to prevent possible condensation damage to the building fabric. For pools with higher occupation levels, extra ventilation may be necessary to remove odours and treatment chemicals. (These points are considered in more detail later in relation to larger, public pools in Section 6.3.) The use of a heat pump in an integrated heating and ventilating scheme, extracting heat from the ventilation exhaust, can be attractive and a number of installations incorporating heat pumps of 4–5 kW input to serve baths having surfaces of 36–64m$^2$ have been reported in some detail [89]. In climates where there is a simultaneous need for pool heating and space cooling, the use of a heat pump to serve both functions has an obvious appeal on grounds of installation cost and energy use.

In indoor pools which are not occupied by many people or for many hours of the day, ventilation requirements are dictated by moisture levels in the air. In this case, a heat pump dehumidifier of the type described in Section 5.6 but of 1–2 kW input can provide considerable energy savings compared with increased ventilation, and can give comfortable conditions. The development and sales of such dehumidifiers in West Germany have been appreciable during the 1970s.

### 5.7 Summary of domestic applications

There are many domestic heat pump applications which are technically feasible and these have been outlined above. Space heating, and particularly space heating where cooling is also required (either in another place or at another time), offers the most widespread, economically attractive use for heat pumps. Dehumidification, where needed, is well done by a heat pump, and there are other possible heat pump uses for domestic swimming pools, although these are not widespread markets.

The use of heat pumps for domestic water heating, and in solar heating schemes, is not competitive with the well-established alternatives, and space- or water-heating heat pumps are not suitable for combining with food storage refrigerators and freezers. In cases where group or district heating schemes are being considered, heat pumps may be attractive and should be included in the options assessed.

### References

[1] Building Research Establishment (1975). *Energy conservation: a study of energy consumption in buildings and possible means of saving energy in housing.* CP 56/75, BRE Watford, UK.
[2] Kernan, G. and Brady, J. (1977). 'Economic evaluation of heat pumps'. *Int. J. Energy Res.* 1(2), 115–25.
[3] Bubenko, J. A. and Fikri, Z. (1975). *Heat pump application in Sweden – Research and Development Needs.* Royal Institute of Technology, Stockholm.
[4] Westh, O. G. (1977). *Heat pumps for space heating – results and conclusions.* Report No. 6, Teknologisk Instituts Forlag, Copenhagen.
[5] Le Febvre, M. (1976). 'Fabricants de pompes à chaleur' (Heat pump manufacturers). *Revue Générale de Thermique* (179), 1003–5.
[6] Spanke, D. and Stoy, B. (1966). 'The heat pump for residential air conditioning throughout the year'. *Int. Z. Elektrowärme,* **24** (6), 181–88. (Part translated as O.A. Trans. 125, Electricity Council, London).
[7] Anon. (1977). 'World heat pump market'. *Heating & Ventilating Engr.* **51** (596), 3.
[8] Building Research Establishment (1981). 'Heat pumps for domestic use' *BRE Digest* 253, BRE, Watford, UK.

[9] McGrath, S. (1977). *Heat pump tests in Irish houses.* Paper (2.3.5) presented at UNIPEDE 4th Electric Space Heating and Air Conditioning Conference, Bordeaux, October 1977.

[10] Nörback, K. (1977). *Results from field tests with heat pumps for space heating in Sweden.* Paper (2.3.6) presented at UNIPEDE 4th Electric Space Heating and Air Conditioning Conference, Bordeaux, October 1977.

[11] Krumme, W. (1974). 'Air-to-water heat pump in a single-family house'. *Elektrowärme Int.* **32** (A1), A35–A41. (Translated as O.A. Trans. 925, Electricity Council, London.)

[12] Kirschbaum, H. S. and Veyo, S. E. (1977). *Investigation of methods to improve heat pump performance and reliability in a northern climate.* Final report, Vols 1, 2, and 3, Westinghouse Electric Corp. Pittsburgh, PA.

[13] Young, D. J. (1979). 'Utility sponsored heat pump research in Canada'. In *Heat pumps and space conditioning systems for the 1990s,* Carrier Corporation, Syracuse, NY, pp. 49–58.

[14] Martin, J. K. and O'Neal, D. L. (1980). *Energy and cost analysis of residential heat pumps in Northern climates,* Oak Ridge National Laboratory, Tennessee.

[15] Jänich, H. (1976). 'Erfahrungen beim Einsatz einer Hauswärmepumpe' (Experience with the use of a domestic heat pump). *Strompraxis* **26** (4), 20–1.

[16] Dratz, H. J. (1976). 'Die weitere Entwicklung von Wasser-Wasser-Wärmepumpen für Einfamilienhäuser' (Further development of water-to-water heat pumps for residences). *Elektrowärme Int.* **32** (A1), A23–A27.

[17] Balke, K. D. (1977). 'Das Grundwasser als Energieträger' (Ground water as an energy carrier). *Brenstoff Wärme Kraft* **29** (5), 191–4.

[18] Jänich, H. (1978). 'Erfahrungen mit Planung, Bau und Betrieb von Wärmepumpen, die also Wärmeträger Grundwasser nutzen' (Experience in the design, installation and operation of heat pumps using ground water as source of heat). *Elektrowärme Int.* **36** (A2), A107–A110.

[19] Heap, R. D. (1977). 'American heat pumps in British houses'. *Elektrowärme Int.* **35** (A2), A77–A81.

[20] Armor, M. (1981). *Heat pumps and houses,* Prism Press, Dorchester, Dorset.

[21] Mountford, D. and Freund, P. (1981). 'The performance of an air-water heat pump installed in an experimental house'. *Build. Serv. Eng. Res. Tech.* **2**(4) 174–80.

[22] Heap, R. D. (1979). 'Heat pumps for houses?' *Build. Res. Pract.* **7** (5), 292–6

[23] Heap, R. D. (1980), 'Development of a domestic heating only heat pump.' *Int. J. Ambient Energy* **1**(2), 89–92.

[24] Freund, P. and Cattell, R. K. (1980). 'The development and testing of a heat pump for heating a single room.' *Energy Research* **4**, 353–62.

[25] McMullan, J. T., Morgan, R. and Hughes, D. W. (1981). 'The discrepancy between heat pump field and test performance: a simulation study'. *Int. J. Energy Research* **5** (1), 83–94.

[26] Didion, D. A. (1979). 'New testing and rating procedures for seasonal performance of heat pumps'. *ASHRAE J.* **21** (9), 40.

[27] Heap, R. D. (1976). 'Heat pumps and housing'. *Building Services Engineer* **44** (4), 80–5.

[28] Gilman, S. F. (Ed) (1978). *Solar energy heat pump systems for heating and cooling buildings.* Pennsylvania State UP, USA.

[29] Andrews, J. W. (1980). *Solar assisted heat pump research and development program in the US,* Brookhaven National Laboratory, Upton, NY.

[30] Davis, C. P. and Lipper, R. I. (1958). 'Sun energy assistance for air-type heat pumps'. *Trans. Am. Soc. Heating and Air Conditioning Engrs.* **64**, 97–110.

## 140    Heat pumps

[31] Cassel, T. A. V., Lorsch, H. G. and Lior, N. (1975). 'Solar heat pump comfort heating systems'. *10th Intersoc. Energy Convers. Eng. Conf. Record* 162–70.

[32] Sakai, I., Takagi, M., Terakawa, J. and Ohue, J. (1976). 'Solar space heating and cooling with bi-heat source heat pump and hot water supply system'. *Solar Energy* **18**, 525–32.

[33] Neal, W. E. J. and Dodson, C. (1977). 'The use of solar energy, a heat pump and thermal store for domestic heating'. *Heating and Ventilating News* **20** (7), 64–6.

[34] Anon. (1980). 'Tech Alert E99: Solar heat pump'. *Engineering* **220** (3), 312.

[35] Szokolay, S. V. (1975). *Solar energy and building*. The Architectural Press, London, and Halsted Press Divn., Wiley, New York.

[36] Seymour-Walker, K. J. (1976). 'Heat pumps'. *Building* **CCXXXI** (39), 119–20.

[37] Bruno, R., Hermann, W., Hörster, H., Kersten, R. and Mahdjuri, F. (1977). *The Philips experimental house: results and experience*. Philips GmBH, Aachen, W. Germany.

[38] Dupagne, A., Hannay, J., Lebrun, J. and Mockels, J., (1977). *Chauffage d'une maison unifamiliale par pompe de chaleur et panneaux solaires* (Heating a single family house by heat pump and solar panels). Paper presented at International Institute of Refrigeration, Commissions B1, B2, E1, Belgrade, November 1977.

[39] Ziegenbein, B. (1977). 'Das BBC-Solarhaus – Aufbau und Betriebser-fahrungengen' (The BBC solar house – design and operating experiences). *Elektrowärme Int.* **35** (A5), A294–297.

[40] Grimm, H. (1977). *'Operating experience with heat pump installations'*. Paper presented at UNIPEDE 4th Electric Space Heating and Air Conditioning Conference, Bordeaux, October 1977.

[41] McLaughlin, T. P. (1976). *A house for the future*. Independent Television Books Ltd, London.

[42] Spielvogel, L. G. (1980). 'The solar bottom line'. *ASHRAE J.* **22** (11), 38–40.

[43] Gillett, W. B. (1978). 'Use of heat pumps with solar collectors for domestic space heating in the UK', *Applied Energy* **4** (3), 187–97.

[44] Packer, M. B. and Glicksman, L. R. (1979). 'An assessment of thermal energy storage in conjunction with heat pumps for residential heating and cooling'. *Energy* **4** (3), 393–9.

[45] Spauschus, H. O. (1979). *Energy efficiency of heat pumps with thermal storage*. Paper presented at XV International Congress of Refrigeration, Venice, Italy, September 1979.

[46] Minturn, R.E., Abbatiello, L. A., Nephew, E. A. and Baxter, V. D. (1980). *ACES 1979 – Capabilities and potential*, ORNL/CON-48 Oak Ridge National Laboratory, Tennessee, USA.

[47] Abbatiello, L. A., Nephew, E. A. and Ballou, M. L. (1981). *Performance and economics of the ACES and Alternative Residential Heating and Air conditioning systems in 115 US cities*, ORNL/CON 52, Oak Ridge National Laboratory, Tennessee, USA.

[48] Baxter, V. D. (1981). *ACES: Final performance report December 1, 1978 through September 15, 1980*, ORNL/CON-64, Oak Ridge National Laboratory, Tennessee, USA.

[49] Strong, D. T. G. (1979). *Development of a directly fired domestic heat pump*. Paper presented at XV International Congress of Refrigeration, Venice, Italy, September 1979.

[50] Zegers, P. (ed.) (1981). *New ways to save energy. The community's energy R & D programme energy conservation* (EUR 7389 EN), Commission of the European Communities, Brussels.

[51] Janssen, H. A. and Oelert, G. (1978). 'Development of a primary energy driven absorption heat pump for domestic heating' (EUR 6326). In *Proceedings of meeting on industrial processes energy conservation research and development,* November 1978, Brussels, pp. 193–204.

[52] Mills, P. (1976). 'Minimum energy houses, the way ahead'. *DOE Construction* **17**, March, 2–7.

[53] Gfeller, R. (1982). 'The possibilities of waste-heat recovery by heat pumps; shown on the basis of several studies and plants realised in Switzerland'. In *Int. Symposium on the Industrial Application of Heat Pumps,* Coventry, UK. BHRA Fluid Engineering, Cranfield, UK, pp. 141–60.

[54] Flohrschütz, R. (1980). 'Recovery of waste heat in sewers by heat pumps' (EUR 7061). In *New ways to save energy. Proceedings of EEC seminar,* EEC, Brussels, p. 102.

[55] Calm, J. M. (1979). 'Heat pump systems for district heating and cooling'. *ASHRAE J.* **21** (9), 54–8

[56] Klaus, H. (1980). 'Experience with monovalent electric heat pumps with air as heat source for 56 apartments'. In *New ways to save energy. Proceedings of EEC seminar,* EEC, Brussels, p. 275.

[57] Freund, P. and Wozniak, S. J. (1980). 'BRE tests heat pump and solar at Basildon'. *Building Services and Environmental Engineer* **3** (3), 26–9.

[58] Vezirishvili, O.Sh. and Khachaturjan, R. A. (1977). *Heat and cold supply of buildings in coastal zone.* Paper presented at UNESCO International Seminar Heat and Mass Transfer in Buildings, Dubrovnik, Yugoslavia, August/September 1977.

[59] Diedrich, H. (1977). *Utilization of heat recovered from waste water by means of heat pumps.* Paper (2.3.2) presented at UNIPEDE 4th Electric Space Heating and Air Conditioning Conference, Bordeaux, October 1977.

[60] Aureille, R. (1976). 'Application des pompes à chaleur à la géothermie' (Heat pumps applications to geothermy). *Revue Générale de Thermique* **XV** (179), 981–8.

[61] Anon. (1978). 'Creil-géothermie et pompes à chaleur' (Creil-geothermy and heat pumps). *Protoclim A* **9** (1), 10–13.

[62] Anon. (1980). 'Earth source heat pumps'. *Sanitar – und Heizungstechnik* **12**, 1112.

[63] Heiburg, O. and Lohsträter, W. (1980). 'Energy conservation by use of a gas engine driven heat pump for an apartment building using outside air as heat source' (EUR 7133). In *New ways to save energy. Proceedings of EEC seminar,* EEC, Brussels, p. 266.

[64] Menkveld, H. J. (1981). *Laboratory test results and practical implications of the use of a gas engine driven compression heat pump.* Paper presented at International Institute of Refrigeration, Commissions B1, B2, E1, E2, Essen, West Germany, September 1981.

[65] Field, A. A. (1980). 'Gas engine drives heat pump in Swiss flats complex'. *Building Services and Environmental Engineer* **3** (3), 30–1.

[66] Korsgaard, A. (1978). 'Special heat pumps' (1) diesel engine driven' (in Danish). *Varme* **43** (1), 16–21.

[67] Petersen, B. (1980). 'Diesel driven heat pump for district heating and for the heating of large housing blocks' (EUR 6740). In *New ways to save energy. Proceedings of EEC seminar,* EEC, Brussels, p. 278.

[68] Courtney, R. G. and Macadam, J. A. (1976). *An economic assessment of long distance heat transport and the utilisation of power station reject heat for district*

*heating.* BRE CP 46/76, Building Research Establishment, Watford, UK.

[69] Courtney, R. G. and Jackman, P. J. (1976). 'A study of three district heating schemes'. *Heating and Ventilating Engr.* **50** (584), 6–14.

[70] HMSO (1977). *District heating combined with electricity generation in the UK.* Energy paper No. 20, Her Majesty's Stationery Office, London.

[71] Courtney, R. G. and Hobson, P. J. (1978). *The performance of 15 district heating schemes'.* BRE CP 34/78, Building Research Establishment, Watford, UK.

[72] McNair, H. P. (1979). 'Comparitive energy consumptions in domestic heating schemes'. *Build. Services and Environmental Engineer* **2** (2), 6–8.

[73] Lorentzen, G. (1981). 'The principles of thermodynamic heating'. *Int. J. Refrig.* **4** (2), 67–72.

[74] Anon. (1962). 'Feasibility studies of the heat pump water heater'. *Edison Electric Institute Bulletin* August, **262**, 269.

[75] Arthur D. Little Inc. (1977). *Study of energy savings options for refrigeration and water heaters,* Vol. 2. PB 269–154, US Department of Commerce, Washington DC.

[76] Electricity Council (1971). *White meter water heating.* ECR/R271, Electricity Council, London.

[77] Freund, P., Leach, S. J. and Seymour-Walker, K. (1976). *Heat pumps for use in buildings.* BRE current paper 19/76, Building Research Establishment, Watford, UK.

[78] Ferranti, B. de (1955). 'Heat pumps in the house'. *Electrical Times* 27 October 627–8.

[79] Gorzelnik, E. F. (1977). 'Heat water with your air conditioner'. *Electrical World* **188** (11), 54–5.

[80] O'Neal, D. L., Haynes, V. O., Hirst, E. and Carney, J. (1979). *Energy and economic effects of residential heat pump water heaters.* (CONF-790107-2), Oak Ridge National Laboratory, Tennessee, USA.

[81] Dunning, R. L., Amthor, F. R. and Doyle, E. J. (1978). *Research and development of a heat pump water heater, volume 1. Final summary report.* ORNL/SUB-7321/1, Energy Utilization Systems Inc., Pittsburg, Pennsylvania, USA.

[82] Gorzelnik, E. F. (1979). 'Heat pump water heater makes debut'. *Electrical World* 15 April, 80–1

[83] Brundrett, G. W. (1977). *Moisture control in buildings – opportunities for a heat pump dehumidifier.* Paper presented at UNESCO International Seminar Heat and Mass Transfer in Buildings, Dubrovnik, Yugoslavia, August/September 1977.

[84] Blundell, C. J. (1978). *Heat exchanger design for a domestic dehumidifier.* ECRC M/1166, Electricity Council Research Centre, Chester, UK.

[85] Blundell, C. J. (1979). *Energy conservation using improved heat pump dehumidifiers.* Paper presented to 2nd International CIB Symposium on Energy Conservation in the Built Environment, Copenhagen, May 1979.

[86] Brundrett, G. W. and Blundell, C. J. (1980), 'An advanced dehumidifier for Britain'. *Heating and Ventilating Engineer* **54** (632), 6–9.

[87] Capaldi, B. (1975). 'Units to ventilate the house and to dry clothes', *Electrical Review* **197** (14), 428–9.

[88] Koehn, O. (1981). 'Supplying hot water from the domestic freezer'. *Building Services and Environmental Engineer* **3** (5), 23.

[89] Rheinisch-Westfälishces Elektrizitätswerk AG, *Data sheets* Sp–10, Sp–11, Sp–12, Sp–13, Sp–15, (in German). RWE, Essen, W. Germany.

# Applications in commerce
# and in public buildings

# 6

Summer cooling is desirable in many commercial and public buildings in all but the most extreme climates. This means that reversible air-conditioners in the form of heat pumps are an obvious choice to provide winter space heating. This has been appreciated for many years, as the history of heat pump applications shows (see Chapter 1), and there are now very many buildings both in Europe and the US in which heat pumping in one form or another is successfully used.

Whilst all that has been said in previous chapters about space heating and about domestic applications may be equally applied to commercial buildings, there are additional opportunities for heat pumping. Many buildings have simultaneous heating and cooling requirements in different areas, and the use of heat pumps to provide heat redistribution can be worth while. Some public buildings have very high ventilation requirements when they are densely occupied, so that heat recovery by heat pump from the ventilation exhaust is worth consideration.

Rather than using outdoor heat sources such as air, water, or ground, many commercial heat pump installations use internal heat sources, and are in the form of heat recovery or heat redistribution rather than heat generating installations, although there is at least one scheme in operation using sea water as the source for heating a cinema and concert hall [1].

Up to the early 1980s the vast majority of heat pumps installed in the UK were reversible air-to-air machines in commercial premises. The total number of installations was around 2000 in mid 1980, mostly of units in the 7–35 kW output range.

Gas-engine-driven heat pumps providing heat to commercial buildings are being used in Europe but are relatively new in Britain, where the relative costs and availability of gas and electricity for commercial use have favoured the electric heat pump.

Simultaneous heating and cooling demands in a single building may, of

143

course, be met by separate heating equipment and cooling equipment, but will generally be more economically met by heat pump systems. These may be fully integrated central systems, partially integrated systems giving ventilation heat recovery in conjunction with other heating and cooling equipment, decentralized systems linked by a closed water loop, or may comprise separate individual modular units using external air as a heat source. The choice of system will depend on the building use and on whether it is being planned or is already built, but increasing awareness of the costs of energy in buildings should ensure an increasing use of heat pumps of all types to reduce energy use.

On a smaller scale there are a number of processes carried out in commercial premises for which heat pumping is appropriate. Dishwashing, laundry work, and food preparation all use considerable amounts of hot water, and recovery of heat from either waste water or from hot humid air may be effective. Dehumidification as an alternative to heating in order to maintain suitable storage conditions in warehouses is another application, and there have also been a number of applications of heat pumps on board ship.

There is now considerable interest not only in extending the range of heat pump applications but also in improving the performance of heat pump systems. As has been emphasized in Chapter 4, heat pump effectiveness is strongly dependent on the design of the whole system in which it is used. Detailed monitoring of installations using outdoor air as a heat source for various types of commercial premises is in progress in Britain and elsewhere. From reported results it is clear that careful attention to control systems and to installation is essential if the full energy-saving benefits of heat pumps are to be realized.

Heat pumps for these applications are readily available. In larger sizes, equipment may be obtained from refrigeration engineering companies, and in smaller sizes, from distributors or manufacturers. In the US, lists of certified equipment are available from the Air Conditioning and Refrigeration Institute (ARI) [2], and in the UK, West Germany, and France, lists of manufacturers have been issued [3–5] in addition to the usual trade buyers guides. Commercial refrigeration engineers are available to install and maintain the equipment.

In this chapter larger buildings having predictable occupancy patterns (offices, hotels, hospitals, etc.) are considered as one group. Smaller buildings with short-term occupancy peaks (shops, restaurants, clubs) are considered as a second group. The use of heat pumps in swimming-bath halls and leisure centres is covered in a third section, and finally a number of more specific miscellaneous applications are listed.

## 6.1 Large buildings

Large buildings requiring heating and cooling include manufacturing areas, offices, hospitals, hotels, schools and cinemas. These have predictable occupancies and known internal temperature requirements which may be met by various types of heating and cooling systems incorporating heat pumps.

### 6.1.1 Centralized systems

Centralized heat pump systems can combine heating, cooling, heat recovery, and water heating. Heat produced within the building can be collected and redistributed and ventilation exhaust heat can be recovered. The basic arrangement of one type of centralized system is shown in Fig. 6.1. A system such as this is well suited to large buildings on compact sites, having high internal energy use for their external surface area. Here most of the annual heating energy can be provided by the redistribution of heat gains from lighting, occupants, and solar radiation. Such systems are especially applicable to continuously occupied buildings requiring steady temperatures.

The heat pump provides heat to a hot-water circuit serving an air heating

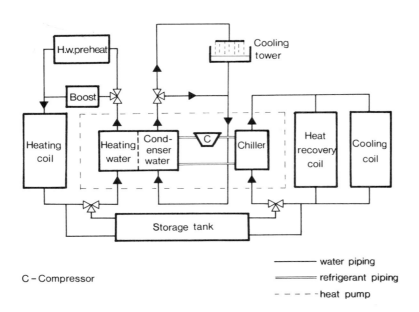

*Fig. 6.1* Centralized heating, cooling, and heat-recovery system.

coil and incorporating auxiliary boost heating and pre-heating of service hot water (i.e. hot water for sinks and basins) if required. The most economical design flow temperature for the hot-water heating circuit is usually 40–45°C [6]. Excess heat may be stored in a hot-water storage tank capable of storing at least enough heat to pre-heat the building on cold mornings. If off-peak electric auxiliary heating is used this may be supplied directly to the storage tank. If the cooling and heat recovery provide an excess of heat to the system, a second heat pump condenser coil is used to reject heat via a cooling tower, but this only happens when the heating need has been met and the storage tank is fully heated. The cooling side of the heat pump provides chilled water to both a cooling coil and a heat recovery coil.

Air is supplied to the rooms of the building by two ducts, one supplying hot air from the heating coil and the other providing cool air from the cooling coil. These air streams are mixed as necessary to provide the required temperatures at each outlet (Fig. 6.2). Air from the rooms is returned via light fittings recovering heat from the lights and keeping them cool, and that proportion of the air which is to be exhausted passes across the heat recovery coil before being rejected to outdoors. This air distribution system is known as 'dual duct', and the whole arrangement is sometimes referred to as a 'bootstrap' heat recovery system. Published examples of such systems include schools, factories, offices and hospitals [7–10], their appropriateness depending both on the type of building and on the local need for summer cooling.

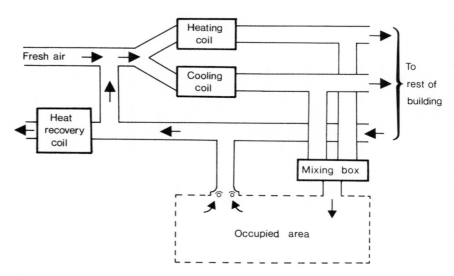

*Fig. 6.2* Air handling circuits for a centralized system such as that shown in Fig. 6.1.

Some buildings have been heated by large, centralized systems for many years. One of these buildings belongs to the Zürich Versicherungsgesellschaft AG and has been heated by a heat pump since 1947 using water from Lake Zürich as the heat source. When new buildings were constructed and the heating system modernized in 1976, both old and new buildings were heated with a heat pump system incorporating five piston compressors and providing approximately 1.5 MW of heat (see Fig. 6.3). As each compressor can be operated at full or half capacity, 10 separate capacity steps are available to provide economical operation over a wide range of heating needs.

Milwaukee schools using centralized heat pump systems to give flexible control together with high comfort standards have been described by Ratai [7, 11]. The schools use dual-duct air-distribution systems, able to provide simultaneous heating and cooling at different parts of the school, and incorporating heat recovery from lights. The systems include complex controls, but the building designs have very low no-heating balance points suggesting that cooling is required for a large part of the school year.

A design described by Bridgers [12] for Albuquerque public schools uses a different approach, the main emphasis being on low costs over the life of the system. Two water chillers acting as heat pumps provide heated or cooled water to each of 22 zones, a single air supply serving each zone with air at the required temperature. Fresh-air cooling is provided when the outdoor

*Fig. 6.3* Machinery room at Zurich. Courtesy of Sulzer Escher Wyss.

temperature is low enough and night time heating is provided by the daytime service hot-water boiler, which has adequate capacity after allowance for the reduced ventilation requirement at night. (In British schools there is no substantial summer cooling requirement, so centralized systems such as these are not appropriate.)

The use of heat pumps in conjunction with solar heating for large commercial buildings is unusual, but there is an example in Pittsburgh, USA where a hospital has a collector area of over 60 m² supplying a glycol solution tank from which heat is extracted and upgraded by a heat pump [13].

There is a wide range of uses for gas fired heat pumps in West Germany and applications exist over a very wide range of heating capacities. Over a hundred were reported to be installed by late 1980. There are also many in Switzerland.

In a sports complex at Paderborn a heat output of 4.65 MW is obtained from a gas input of 2.4 MW in a large well-water-source heat pump which is combined with a heat recovery system [14, 15]. Government buildings at Meckenheim use a large gas-fired absorption unit supplying around 1.7 MW as water at 57°C, with a ground-source coil of 16 000 m² area. This system was reported to achieve a c.o.p. of 1.6 in early 1981.

Centralized systems were first designed to overcome high energy costs for buildings using independent central-heating and cooling systems. These were frequently tall buildings with large glazed areas, suffering from over-heating on a the sunny side and needing heat on the shaded side. Interlinked heat recovery systems gave lower energy use than separate heating and cooling plant, but these improvements depended on the building's charac-teristics and on the quality of the control system. With poor control, it is quite possible in mild weather to take in ventilation air, split it into two streams which are unnecessarily heated and cooled, mix the streams to give the outdoor temperature again, extract heat unnecessarily from the exhaust air, and reject the extracted heat at the cooling tower – all to no heating or cooling effect. Even with good controls, the mixing of heated and cooled air to produce an intermediate temperature is thermodynamically inefficient, and the control complexity is such that faulty operation giving high energy use is not unusual. In the late 1960s centralized systems were being improved, for example by using variable air volume (VAV) rather than variable air temperature to regulate heat output.

At about the same time the 'Integrated Environmental Design' (IED) concept was developing in which a new building is regarded as a single design project incorporating function, layout, lighting, structure, thermal insulation, and comfort control, all to be worked out in relation to each other rather than as isolated design exercises [9]. In Britain this approach has led to more compact office buildings with good levels of thermal insulation, reduced solar gains and good levels of artificial lighting, and can give reduced capital costs and lower running costs than earlier non-IED buildings. By 1972 there were 81 IED buildings reported at various stages of construction in Britain, the majority being office buildings [16]. These typically housed between 100 and 400 occupants (although a few were much larger or smaller), and had a net heating requirement below about 4°C in a climate with a winter design temperature of −1 to −4°C.

One of the first examples of an IED building in Britain was the Merseyside and North Wales Electricity Board (MANWEB) head office at Chester (Fig. 6.4). It incorporates a single-temperature air-distribution network, combined with a chilled water circuit. The central cooling plant, operating as a heat pump, incorporates two three-stage centrifugal compressors providing heated or cooled water to the main air heating and cooling coils. Each compressor can provide approximately 1 MW of heating in winter design conditions [17].

The air distribution temperature is set to provide the basic heating or cooling requirement (in this building cooling is the predominant need), and the chilled-water circuit provides additional cooling to individual areas and is controlled at the outlets to give the required temperature for that particular area. Extract air is drawn across light fittings to recover heat and is passed through a heat recovery coil before being exhausted. The amount of fresh air introduced is varied to take maximum advantage of 'free' cooling, and is greatest in mild weather conditions. At times when heating is required

*Fig. 6.4* MANWEB head office at Chester. Courtesy Merseyside and North Wales Electricity Board.

the chilled-water circuits are used to circulate heated water overnight to provide pre-heating from off-peak electricity. The system is designed to maintain 24°C and 55% r.h. in summer and 21°C and 40% r.h. in winter. The energy use in this building at 178 kWh m$^{-2}$ (Table 6.1) is very low for the comfort and lighting standards maintained [18] and may be compared with figures of 232 and 276 kWh m$^{-2}$ for the air-conditioned areas of two other large air-conditioned buildings, the energy consumptions of which were studied in detail in the late 1960s [19].

*Table 6.1* MANWEB Head Office, Chester.

| | |
|---|---|
| Building area gross | 15890m$^2$ |
| Number of occupants | 1200 |
| Energy use (1977): | |
|    lighting (750 lux, 390 kW) | 1357 MWh |
|    air-conditioning | 1180 MWh |
|    miscellaneous | 294 MWh |
|    total | 2831 MWh |
| Overall annual energy use 178 k Wh m$^{-2}$ | |

### 6.1.2 *Partially integrated systems*

In some buildings with very high fresh-air ventilation requirements, the full heating load may be too large to be met economically by heat pumping. Laundries, cinemas, and swimming-pool halls may come into this category, although there are special possibilities in the latter case as will be seen later (Section 6.3.1). Hospitals may also have high ventilation requirements because of (possibly unfounded) infection worries with a central air-handling system. In these cases partially integrated central systems in which a heat pump is used to recover heat from ventilation exhaust air may be used. Such systems must compete with less expensive heat recovery devices such as heat recovery wheels and run-around coils (simple heat exchangers with an intermediate working fluid usually water or brine), and can only do so effectively if there is a need for the higher temperature heat which the heat pump can produce (for domestic water heating, for example). Specialized ventilation heat recovery applications also exist in the mining industry where mine exhausts can provide a useful source of heat [20].

### 6.1.3 *Decentralized closed-loop systems*

The decentralized, closed-loop, water-source, heat pump system is an ingenious combination of central cooling and heating plant and decentral-

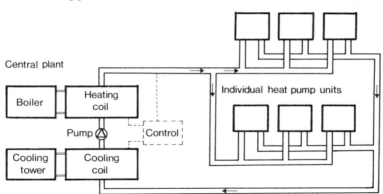

*Fig. 6.5* Multiple unit decentralized heat pump system using a closed water loop.

ized heat recovery and control. The basic concept is shown in Fig. 6.5. Individual water-source reversible heat pumps are installed in place of conventional heat emitters and are linked by a common circulating water source. If heating is required at some locations and cooling at others, the overall requirement at the central heating or cooling plant on the loop will be small, and a small boiler and a cooling tower are usually provided [21, 22].

The water loop operates typically at around 25°C needing no thermal insulation and being relatively easily installed in existing buildings. The individual heat pumps may be wall or ceiling mounted (Fig. 6.6) and provide

*Fig. 6.6* Wall-mounted 'Versatemp' heat pump unit. Courtesy of Temperature Ltd.

an independent choice of heating or cooling at each point, which may be a small office area or a hotel room. The heat pumps are individually controlled by the user to meet the local requirement at any particular time. The central plant is small resulting in space savings, and maintenance work on an individual unit does not affect the operation of other units. The individual units are available in a choice of sizes from around 2.5–5.5 kW heating capacity (1.5–4.5 kW cooling capacity) and many large installations exist. A combined antiques sales centre and office block in Paris uses 2000 units of which 1200 are floor mounted and 800 are concealed in ceiling areas. A typical floor-mounted installation is shown in Fig. 6.7 and the nineteenth century exterior of the otherwise new structure is seen in Fig. 6.8.

Decentralized closed-loop systems may be combined with centralized equipment on a single site, as is done in Provident Hospital, Baltimore [10]. Here, an all fresh-air ventilation system with heat recovery serves the central core of the hospital, but decentralized units serve individual patients' rooms which are more widely scattered and have a greater diversity of use. A decentralized closed-loop system has been used at Kelsterbach, West Germany [23] in conjunction with a separate ventilation heat recovery

*Fig. 6.7*   A typical office installation. Courtesy of Temperature Ltd.

*Fig. 6.8*  Le Centre d'Affaires le Louvre, Place du Palais Royal, Paris. Courtesy of Temperature Ltd.

system using a regenerative heat exchanger to provide heating and cooling in a school building.

### 6.1.4 *Modular, external-source heat pumps*

In buildings which may be split into separate, relatively small zones, each with easy access to outdoor air, completely decentralized or 'modular' heat pump systems using outdoor air as a heat source may be preferable to a complex central system. Capital costs are likely to be lower, separate control of separate zones is easily and reliably achieved, and in the event of breakdown only a part of the building is affected, reducing the need for immediate repair. The shorter air-distribution paths needed result in a reduction in fan power contributing to lower energy use.

One example of a 'modular' heat pump system in Britain in which four air-to-air pumps serve a first-floor office of 641 m$^2$ floor area has been monitored in detail [24]. Each heat pump had a heating output of 14.5 kW (at 7°C outdoor temperature) and a cooling power of 13.8 kW. The heat pump heating capacity was approximately 80% of the design heat loss of 54 kW, and 24 kW of direct electric supplementary heating was added to each heat pump to provide a good margin for rapid pre-heating. The cooling load of 50.5 kW was met entirely by the heat pumps. The monitored energy use in

*Table 6.2* Office Energy Consumption, June 1976–May 1977.

|  | *MWh* | *kWh m$^{-2}$* |
|---|---|---|
| Compressor & outdoor fan: | | |
| heating | 38.8 | 60.6 |
| cooling | 10.2 | 15.9 |
| Indoor fan: | | |
| heating | 10.8 | 16.8 |
| cooling | 3.6 | 5.6 |
| Supplementary heat | 37.8 | 59.0 |
| Lighting and power | 24.9 | 38.9 |
| Total | 126.1 | 196.8 |
| Estimated saving due to heat pump | 59.8 | 93.3 |

this office over the period June 1976 to May 1977 was as shown in Table 6.2.

As is seen from the table, the heat pump provides substantial energy savings. However, 43% of the total heating energy is supplied by the supplementary heaters, most of this being for morning pre-heat after night switch-off. On a cold day, over 70% of the electricity used for heating is used by the supplementary heaters, and in this case there would almost certainly be both cost and energy savings if the heat pumps were to run continuously overnight on thermostatic control rather than being switched off. In milder weather some night switch-off would be worth while, so there is a case for a control system which optimizes the time of morning switch-off, dependent on the prevailing weather condition. (Such control systems are available. See 'Guides to equipment suppliers' in the Bibliography.) The overall energy use is already competitive with a central system in a larger building, and with attention to improved controls could be reduced even further.

In Britain and countries with similar summer conditions where full air conditioning is not needed in schools, trends in school-building layout and design can still favour the use of heat pumps. Changes in British schools to lower amounts of glazing and more compact layouts with higher occupation densities have led to a need for improved mechanical ventilation systems with, if possible, reduced amounts of floor area devoted to building services. Reversible air-source heat pumps may be roof mounted and are able to meet both ventilation and heating requirements. The cooling facility eliminates any summer overheating which may arise, and which would otherwise lead to open windows and consequent noise and wind distractions. A number of local authorities are currently assessing heat pumps in schools in order to find the most appropriate systems for Britain [25].

For any given 'large' building the choice between centralized, closed loop water source and modular heat pump systems is not necessarily obvious. The central system is probably best avoided if a high degree of flexibility of use is anticipated, and the modular approach may be best where it can be installed easily, although for existing compact buildings requiring a new installation, the closed-loop system has considerable attractions. The centralized system is most likely to be appropriate in large, new, purpose-designed buildings of more than two storeys.

## 6.2 Shops and clubs

Smaller commercial premises, such as shops, clubs, and restaurants, share a number of relevant characteristics. In many countries they require both cooling and heating, the need at a particular time being dependent on both weather and occupancy level. In addition, they are on occasions very densely occupied, and as a consequence sometimes need a high fresh-air ventilation rate. The provision of comfortable conditions directly affects the profitability of the business concerned, as it can influence the customer's decision to return on another occasion. All of these characteristics favour the use of heat pumps for heating, cooling and ventilation. They are often more economical to install and easier to control than separate heating and cooling systems, and in addition have lower running costs. They may be arranged to provide large quantities of fresh-air ventilation at times of high occupancy, or may incorporate electrostatic or other air-cleaning devices within a recirculating air system, depending on the requirements of the particular installation. Possibly because of these advantages, which mean that even a poorly designed heat pump system can compete well with the alternatives, insufficient attention is sometimes given to system design and controls, and part of the heat pump potential for saving energy can be lost.

The cost of heat pumps in commercial premises is very dependent on the complexity of design and on the capacities required, but examination of a range of British installations covering areas from 20 m$^2$ to 1200 m$^2$ showed a typical installed cost around £50 per square metre in 1980. Some larger installations were very much less than this figure, values below £10 per square metre being occasionally reported.

A good example of heat pump installation is in a British Legion Club in South Wales (Fig. 6.9). The single-storey building is served by three roof-mounted 17 kW reversible air-to-air heat pumps, with 3 × 6 kW electric supplementary heaters [26]. Although the club must be heated prior to the arrival of up to 400 members, once that number is present cooling is soon required. Air distribution via 18 discharge points, supplying 4300 m$^3$ h$^{-1}$ to the 3000 m$^3$ room, ensures good temperature uniformity despite differing activities within the room. There is an arrangement of ventilation dampers to vary the amount of fresh air taken in, permitting external air to provide

*Fig. 6.9* Clubroom served by heat pump. Courtesy Lennox Industries Ltd.

cooling and save compressor energy use whenever possible, and giving a minimum of 12% fresh air in the air supplied to the room.

The use of a heat pump in a modern British shop has been described in detail as part of the Electricity Council's evaluation of heat pumps [27]. The shop has a gross area of 546 m$^2$ and comprises a ground floor sales area with a storeroom and staff facilities above. There is a total lighting load of 13.7 kW, and the shop layout is such that artificial lighting is needed at all times. A single heat pump of 33 kW nominal cooling capacity and 29 kW heating capacity (at 7°C outdoor temperature) is supplemented by 15 kW of direct electric heating.

Warm air is provided to the sales area and is exhausted partly via the stockroom. As the goods sold are not perishable, cooling is not provided to the stockroom, only to the sales area and staff room. As in the previous example, fresh-air cooling is used whenever outdoor temperatures are sufficiently low. The overall energy use in this shop over a full year is shown in Table 6.3, and is typical of levels to be expected if heat pumps are used in many shops in Britain or in countries having similar climates. Although these energy-use figures are favourable, detailed analysis showed that as in the office installation quoted in Section 6.1.4, provision of an optimum start

*Table 6.3* Annual energy use in a British shop [27].

|  | *MWh* | *kWh m*$^{-2}$ |
|---|---|---|
| Lighting and small power | 52.7 | 96.5 |
| Heat pump heating | 11.4 | 20.8 |
| Heat pump cooling | 3.4 | 6.3 |
| Direct heater battery | 3.3 | 6.0 |
| Additional fans and heaters | 12.5 | 22.9 |
| Total for heating and ventilating | 30.6 | 56.0 |
| Overall total | 83.3 | 152.5 |
| Estimated saving due to heat pump | 17.7 | 32.7 |

control for morning pre-heating and means for cutting out fresh-air ventilation during the pre-heating would give even better results, reducing energy use and reducing maximum electricity demand.

In the UK heat pumps have become increasingly popular in shops in the past few years (for example, Fig. 6.10). A combination of increasing oil

*Fig. 6.10* Interior of a shop serviced by a heat pump installation. Courtesy of Martin the Newsagent Ltd.

prices and availability problems with commercial gas supplies has led many major multiple groups to adopt heat pumps as their standard heating and cooling equipment. Apart from the obvious advantages in operating costs, allowances against corporation tax help to reduce installation costs, and careful design to take advantage of electricity tariffs such as the maximum demand relief tariff ensures a very attractive return on investment.

Control of supplementary heating is particularly important, as this has a large effect on the expensive demand component of the electricity tariff. Depending on the tariffs available in particular countries, the use of night-time pre-heating, of interlinked supplementary heating and lighting controls, and of low-power supplementary heating during defrosting should all be assessed at the design stage to minimize running costs. A little extra money spent on controls is likely to prove a first class investment. Some British retail groups have over a hundred installations and the increasing level of new installations in 1979–82 helped to hold purchase costs of equipment relatively steady in a time of general rapid inflation.

Single package air-to-air pumps are readily available in the 6–60 kW heat output range. These are very suitable for rooftop installation on commercial buildings. Typical units are shown in Figs 6.11 and 6.12.

The design flexibility possible with this equipment is well illustrated by a hypermarket installation at Havant, England. The hypermarket has a conditioned area of 11 500 m² and the temperature control system combines heat recovery, heat pumps, and gas-fired heating. When cooling is required, eight reversible heat pumps are used. For heating, the first choice is heat recovered from the condensers of the store's refrigeration plant. As soon as this heat becomes insufficient, the heat pumps are used, and on occasions when these two are insufficient, supplementary heat is provided from liquid petroleum gas. A microprocessor-based energy management system controls the plant.

Another example is a store in Reading where an area of about 17 000 m² is served by 25 roof-mounted air-to-air units. The total cooling capacity is 1.32 MW, the heating capacity is 780 kW at −1°C ambient temperature, and each unit is separately controlled. The building includes separate refrigeration plant and heat recovered from this provides warehouse heating and part of the hot-water requirement [28].

In shops or restaurants where waste heat is available from frozen-food storage areas or from kitchen cooling, heat pumps may profitably be considered for heat recovery to provide either space heating or hot-water supplies. In a study of food-storage refrigeration [29], it was found that 100 kW of heating was available for recovery in a supermarket which had a space-heating requirement of up to 150 kW – considerable energy savings can clearly be achieved in such cases. Heat recovery to provide water heating is only feasible if hot water is stored until it is required, and is worth

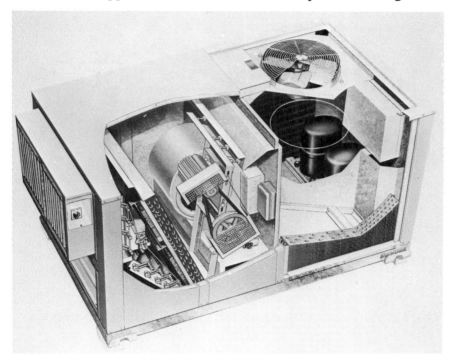

*Fig. 6.11* Small packaged heat pump unit. Courtesy of Lennox Industries Ltd.

consideration in premises such as restaurants and laundries where there is a regular hot-water demand. Such schemes have been used over at least three decades. Although a heat pump could provide water at a high temperature (if necessary by using a multi-stage vapour compression cycle), use of an intermediate temperature store for recovered heat and a final 'topping up' direct heater is likely to be preferable.

## 6.3 Recreation and leisure centres

The heating and cooling of leisure centres, sports halls, and swimming baths offer considerable scope for the use of heat pumping techniques. The use of standard air-to-air heat pumps or water-source heat pumps in sports halls does not differ from similar heat pump applications in the other types of large buildings which have already been considered. Indoor swimming-pool halls can incorporate heat pumps for pool water heating, for ventilation heat recovery, for dehumidification, or for any combination of these. Outdoor pools only require pool heating, but where a sports complex includes both a

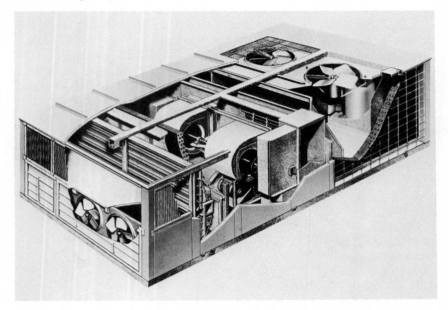

*Fig. 6.12* Large packaged heat pump unit. Courtesy of Lennox Industries Ltd.

pool and an ice rink, a heat pump may provide pool heating and rink freezing from an integrated system. Heat pumps for swimming pools have the dual advantages of low heat pump condensing temperatures and high power levels, so that a high c.o.p. is possible.

### 6.3.1 *Indoor swimming pools*

The scope for water heating, air dehumidification, and ventilation heat recovery using heat pumps for small pools has been mentioned in Section 5.8. In larger pools, controls and water-treatment systems are more complex, and integration of heating and ventilating systems present special problems. Both the problems and some possible solutions using heat pumps have been extensively considered. Various combinations of heat exchanger, heat recovery and heat pumps have been compared and analysed by Braham who concludes that most combinations offer great advantages over traditional systems with relatively small differences in payback periods between different heat pump systems [30].

In Britain, the pool water temperature recommended by the Sports Council is 27°C, with a hall air temperature of 28°C, although frequently air temperatures are a little lower to minimize operating costs. These conditions give an annual water loss from the pool surface of 2400 litre m$^{-2}$ and a latent heat loss of 1640 kWh m$^{-2}$, requiring a ventilation rate of 0.015 m$^3$ s$^{-1}$ for each square metre of wetted area. If pool-hall heating and ventilation is provided without ventilation air recirculation or heat recovery, the total use of energy is considerable, possible as high as 10 000 kWh m$^{-2}$ of pool surface annually.

The basic requirements in the pool hall are the provision of sufficient fresh air to prevent build-up of odours, and the maintenance of a humidity level low enough to prevent condensation in the building structure and on windows. The amount of air required for odour control depends on the water treatment system: if some of the chlorine treatment is replaced by ozone treatment, a considerable reduction in necessary ventilation rates may be possible, although details of alternative water treatment processes are beyond the scope of this book. The use of energy for humidity control may be minimized, either by heat pump dehumidification or by heat recovery from exhaust air. A fully integrated system using heat pumping can reduce energy use to 2500 kWh m$^{-2}$ annually or less.

The simplest heat pump system for a pool hall is a heat pump dehumidifier allowing reduced ventilation rates – this is appropriate for smaller or less frequently occupied pools, and the operation of the dehumidifier would be similar to that described in Section 5.6. For larger pools, this may be improved by incorporating dehumidification in the air-handling system, as is shown in Fig. 6.13. Further improvements to this system are possible, first by incorporating heat recovery between the exhaust outlet and fresh-air inlet ducts, using runaround coils at the pool-hall air outlet and between the

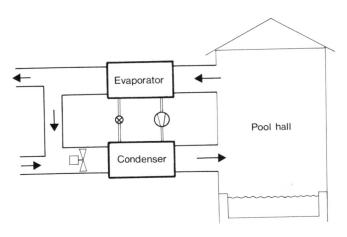

*Fig. 6.13* Swimming-pool hall air handling system, with dehumidification and heat recovery.

heat pump coils. Ventilation reduction is limited by the fresh-air requirements for odour control. When designing pools for high occupancy, full fresh-air ventilation may be combined with a heat recovery system, the heat being used for pool water, showers, and space heating, one such system being shown in Fig. 6.14. In this scheme, runaround coils recover heat which could only otherwise be recovered by using an uneconomically large heat pump.

Appropriate combinations of ventilation control, dehumidification, and heat recovery may be found for pools of all sizes, both new and existing, to enable comfort standards to be maintained at lower cost and for lower energy use than is possible with simple heating and ventilation. This combination of higher standards and lower running costs has led to an appreciable heat pump market in Germany and other parts of Europe, and a number of installations are in operation in Britain.

The Eastbourne leisure pool was opened in 1977. Here, a heat pump installation started operation in 1980 and was publicized as the hundredth electric heat pump installation in British pool halls. This led to a reduction of nearly 50% in running costs over the first year of operation. A payback period of 3.7 years is claimed. There are three pools of total area 780 m$^2$ and the system incorporates a heat pump to supply approximately 0.25 MW of heat to pool water, hall air, and hot-water services.

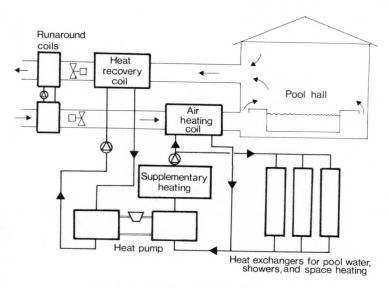

*Fig. 6.14* Integrated heat recovery for swimming pools.

### 6.3.2 *Outdoor pools*

Outdoor swimming pools are popular, and both their popularity and their economics can be improved if water temperatures can be maintained at higher levels for a longer season. Heat pumps using either air or local water sources may be used to provide pool heating at a low energy cost.

A number of outdoor pools of 700–2000 m² surface area in Germany are heated by heat pumps, using air or water heat sources and electric drives [31], and one at Dortmund which has provoked particular interest is driven by a gas engine [32]. It is claimed that the Dortmund installation has an effective energy efficiency of up to 235%, by combining an air-to-water heat pump with engine exhaust-heat recovery. The cost of the engine itself is appreciable, and the overall economics of such schemes depend strongly on local gas and electricity tariffs. The low level of energy use makes the installation worth detailed description.

The basic system layout is shown in Fig. 6.15. The gas engine, seen in Fig. 3.3 p. 39 has an output of 83 kW, and operates at an efficiency of 30%. The compressor, a 12-cylinder reciprocating unit using R22, enables heat to be drawn from the outdoor air at 8°C and pumped to keep the pool at 24°C with a c.o.p. (presumed to exclude fans and water pumps) of 6, and the output of the system is augmented by the recovery of engine exhaust heat up to the equivalent of 55% of the calorific value of the gas input. The approximate power levels at each stage are given in Table 6.4.

The evaporation temperature of the refrigerant is − 2°C when the outdoor air is 8°C and 80% relative humidity, and its condensing temperature is then 28°C. The exhaust-heat recovery unit cools the gases from 600°C to 70°C.

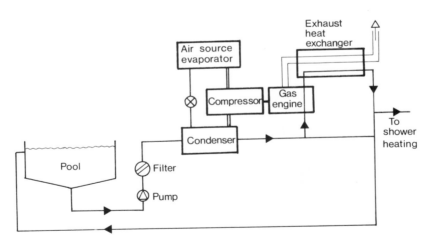

*Fig. 6.15* Layout of Dortmund pool heating system. After Ruhrgas AG [32].

*Table 6.4* Dortmund heat pump

| | | |
|---|---|---|
| Calorific value of gas input (kW) | 280 | |
| Engine output (kW) | 83 | |
| Compressor power (kW) | 75 ⎫ | total heat |
| Heat from outdoor air (kW) | 420 ⎬ | to pool |
| Heat recovered from engine exhaust (kW) | 90 ⎭ | 585 kW |

Design pool-water temperature is 24°C, but a hotter supply to showers is also provided from the heat recovery unit as needed. Outdoor air is cooled to 2°C at the evaporators, of which there are two, which are housed alongside the plant room and which require an air flow of 13 000 m³ h⁻¹ – the air-handling unit is seen in Fig 6.16. The combined effects of fans and water pumps will reduce the overall energy ratio to less than 2. Although such a system may work effectively to heat an indoor pool, the exhaust-heat recovery could be difficult to integrate into a controlled system including heat recovery in an indoor pool hall. When dehumidification without heating was required, the high temperature waste heat could not be used and the overall efficiency would be reduced.

Another example is the Jacob outdoor pool at Constance, Switzerland

*Fig. 6.16* Air handling units and plant house for Dortmund swimming-pool heat pump.

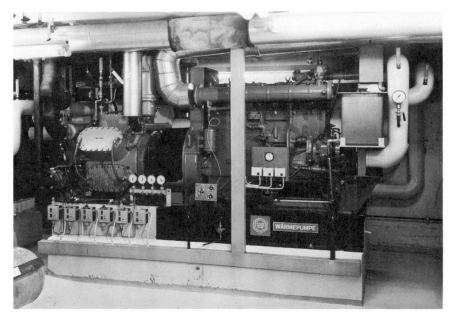

*Fig. 6.17* Gas-engine-driven heat pump for the Jacob outdoor pool at Constance. Courtesy of Sulzer Escher Wyss.

where two 117 kW gas engines are each coupled to ammonia compressors in an installation providing 480 kW of heating for pools and cloakroom facilities. The engine room is shown in Fig. 6.17. Heat is extracted from an ice rink, a hot spring, waste water, and engine reject heat.

There is some interest in gas-fired heat pumps for pools in Britain and the first practical application started operation in Colchester in 1980 [33]. It is not yet clear whether this market will develop or whether it will be limited by gas availabilty to the UK commercial sector.

### 6.3.3 Ice rinks

The combination of ice rink refrigeration and swimming-pool or other heating is a particularly satisfactory use of heat pumping. Wherever there is a need for heating in conjunction with an ice rink installation considerable savings, in both capital and running costs, are achieved by using an integrated heat pump scheme.

An installation at the 8th Olympic Winter Games in California was reported in 1960 in which 11 150 m² of rink surface was served by a 1.9 MW heat pump installation. The heat extracted from the rink was used to heat spectator enclosures, provide general space heating to service buildings, pre-heat water supplies to 38°C and also to provide a snow-clearing system for the roof [34]. Considerable savings in installation costs were claimed by comparison with separate heating and refrigeration installations.

A more recent installation in Germany provides heat to two swimming pools of total surface area 750 m² [35]. A heat pump was provided, first using river water as a heat source and later taking heat from an 840 m² skating rink. Once again, installation costs were reduced compared with separate systems and a reported coefficient of performance of up to 6.5 gives low running costs. The equipment is able to take advantage of off-peak electricity, and demand control is incorporated to ensure economic operation.

## 6.4 Other commercial applications

Heat pumps have been used in a variety of commercial applications in addition to those specifically discussed in the preceding sections. Factories and warehouses have been designed with full heat recovery schemes, such as those described in Section 6.1, particularly for products such as tobacco for which close environmental control is required. Waste process heat has been used to provide space heating in factories (see for example Section 7.1). Heat pump dehumidifiers have been used to maintain low humidity in warehouses, as an energy saving alternative to winter heating. In addition to these general applications, several specific uses of heat pumps are worth mentioning.

The provision of hot-water supplies in commercial premises in which there is a refrigeration requirement is an obvious area for heat pump application. Heat reclaim from refrigerated storage cabinets can supply hot-water storage tanks in systems with 1–3-year payback periods [36]. In the case of public houses a good case can be made for using a heat pump to combine cellar cooling with hot-water supply, a system not very different in principle from the domestic Ferranti unit of the 1950s (see Section 1.3), which looks as though it will have more widespread commercial application in the 1980s.

Cooling is required to store dairy products and in milk bars and similar establishments hot water is needed for washing up and cleaning. The same is true of a wide range of retail outlets handling a wide range of goods. In all these cases a heat pump may be used to meet both the cooling and heating requirements [37, 38]. Meat processing also offers scope for heat recovery from storage area cooling equipment to provide water for space heating [39, 40]. Heat recovery from commercial dishwashers not only saves energy but also improves the local working environment [41].

Heat pumps have been used on farms since the early 1950s [32] and have proved worthwhile not only in milk production but wherever there is a year-round application such as combined greenhouse heating and store cooling. Alternate heating or cooling for maintenance of livestock house temperatures has also been provided by heat pumps. The application of heat pumping to grain drying is considered along with other similar drying processes in Chapter 7.

There have been a number of marine applications of heat pumps possibly the first being in German and British submarines during World War II [42]. These were reported to be aimed at minimizing battery loads while submerged. More modern submarine applications could include water distillation plant and space-conditioning equipment, and may use thermoelectric rather than vapour compression equipment if silence is more important than efficiency. Installations in surface ships include HMS *Vidal* in 1947 on which a 56 kW motor provided 200 kW of heating. A large heat pump unit provided 2.6 MW of heating on the *Southern Cross*. These installations save energy compared with direct electric heating from diesel generators but probably not compared with direct steam heating where that is available. No doubt heat pumps can be combined with exhaust heat recovery in diesel-driven vessels, although such applications are not readily found in published heat pump literature.

It is apparent from this brief list that heat pumps may be considered wherever either combined heating and cooling or heat recovery are required. The economic feasibility will depend on the particular application, and some methods of assessing this are discussed further in Chapter 8. The longer the annual hours of use and the better matched the heating and cooling requirements, the more likely is any particular application to be economic.

## References

[1] Vezirishvili, O. Sh. and Khachaturjan, R. A. (1977). *Heat and cold supply of buildings in coastal zone.* Paper presented at UNESCO International Seminar Heat and Mass Transfer in Buildings, Dubrovnik, Yugoslavia, August/September 1977.

[2] Air-Conditioning and Refrigeration Institute (1977). *Directory of certified unitary products.* ARI, Arlington, VA, USA.

[3] Electricity Council (1978). *Guidelines to the selection of external source air/air heat pumps in commercial premises.* EC3612, Electricity Council, London.

[4] Anon. (1977). 'Wärmepumpenanlagen' (Heat pump specifications). *Technik am Bau* **5** (August), 475–80.

[5] Plan Construction (1977). *Concours pour l'experimentation des pompes à chaleur dans l'habitat* (Heat pump trials in housing). Ministère de l'Equipement, Paris.

[6] Bowen, J. L. (1975). 'Energy conservation in the seventies'. *Refrigeration and Air Conditioning* **78** (925), 52–5, 60.

[7] Ratai, W. R. (1975). 'Heat pump system judged best for compact school' *Heating, Piping, Air Conditioning* April, reprint.

## 168 Heat pumps

[8] Bazzoni, J. P. (1966). 'Newspaper plant heating is hot off the press'. *Heating, Piping, Air Conditoning* **38** (October), 122–5.

[9] Sherratt, A. F. C. (Ed) (1974). *Integrated environment in building design.* Applied Science, London.

[10] Platts, J. R. (1977). 'Why an electric hospital'. *Heating and Ventilating Engr.* **51** (595), 9–11.

[11] Ratai, W. R. (1972). 'Heat pump saves school energy'. *Building Systems Design* **69** (March), 6–9.

[12] Bridgers, F. H. (1973). 'Energy conservation: pay now, save later'. *ASHRAE J.* **15** (10), 47–52.

[13] Anon. (1981). 'A solar-assisted system: even the sun needs help'. *ASHRAE J.* **22** (11), 49.

[14] Anon. (1981). 'Ruhrgas installation'. *IK.Z*, **15/16,** 5.

[15] Critolph, R. (1980). 'Reviewing developments in engine driven heat pumps'. *Building Services and Environmental Engineer* **3** (3), 23–4.

[16] Shepherd, L. (1973). 'Review of integrated buildings in Great Britain'. *Elektrowärme Int.* **31** (A1), A33–A37.

[17] Merseyside and North Wales Electricity Board (1971). *Presenting the all-electric environment at Chester.* MANWEB, Chester, UK.

[18] Private communication from MANWEB, Chester, UK.

[19] Milbank, N. O. (1968). *Energy consumption and cost in 2 large air-conditioned buildings.* CP40/68, Building Research Establishment, Watford, UK.

[20] Anon. (1970). 'Heat pump application at Old Ben 26'. *Coal Mining & Processing* **7** (5), 36–7.

[21] Soule, J. P. (1971). 'Closed loop water source heat pump system'. *ASHRAE J.* **13** (9), 83–94.

[22] Temperature Ltd. (1972). *'Versatemp' Applications Manual.* Temperature Ltd, London.

[23] Main-kraftwerke AG, *Gesamtschule Kelsterbach-dezentral Klimatisiert durch Kleinwärmepumpen* (decentralised air-conditioning using small heat pumps). Data Sheet Sch-201, MKW, Frankfurt a. M.-Höchst, W. Germany.

[24] Electricity Council (1977). *The performance of packaged heat pumps in an office building.* ECR/R1105, Electricity Council, London.

[25] Anon. (1977). 'Applying heat pumps to schools'. *Electrical Times* No. 4415, 11 February, 4.

[26] Lennox Industries Ltd (1975). *First Lennox heat pump installation by Cool-Rite Ltd., British Legion Club chooses economical answer to comfort conditioning.* Press Release, Lennox Industries Ltd, Basingstoke, UK.

[27] Electricity Council (1978). *The performance of a packaged heat pump in a high street store.* ECR/R1127, Electricity Council, London.

[28] Anon. (1982). 'News Item'. *Building Services and Environmental Engineering* **4** (5), 4.

[29] Electricity Council (1976). *Characteristics of food storage refrigeration in supermarkets.* ECR/R969, Electricity Council, London.

[30] Braham, G. D. (1982). 'Heat recovery technology for swimming pools by the application of heat pumps'. In *International Symposium on the Industrial Application of Heat Pumps,* Coventry, UK. BHRA Fluid Engineering, Cranfield, UK, pp. 239–42.

[31] Rheinisch-Westfälisches Elektrizitätswerk AG. *Data sheets,* Sp–1, Sp–3, Sp–5, (in German), RWE, Essen, W. Germany.

[32] Ruhrgas AG (1977). *Europe's first gas heat pump put into operation in a*

*swimming pool in Dortmund*. Translation No. T4306/BGC/1977, British Gas, London.

[33] Metcalf, J. H. (1981). 'Heating with a gas engine driven heat pump'. *Heating and Ventilating Engineer* Feb., 14–15.

[34] Vandament, D. (1960). 'Olympic heat pump installation warms spectators, melts snow'. *Heating, Piping and Air Conditioning,* **32** (February), 99–102.

[35] Eicke, K. (1974). 'Heat pump system serving both a skating rink and an indoor swimming pool'. *Elektrowärme Int.* **32** (A3), A151–A154. (Translated as O.A. Trans. 941, Electricity Council, London.)

[36] Anon. (1979). 'Hot water from refrigeration plant'. *Heating and Ventilating Review* March, 67.

[37] Hess, H. (1976). 'Untersuchung zur Optimierung der Energiebedarfsdeckung in Molkereibetrieben' (Optimizing the supply of energy in dairies). *Elektrowärme Int.* **34** (A5), A236–A244.

[38] Anon. (1964). 'Heat pumps for farms'. *Electrical Times* **146**, 17 September, p. 417.

[39] Fischer, K. (1976). 'Ausnutzung der kaltemaschinen-Abwarme in einem Fleischereibetrieb' (Utilization of waste heat from refrigerating units in a butchery). *Elektrowärme Int.* **84** (A5), A 247–A248.

[40] Lehringer, K. (1976). 'Verfahren zur Wärmerückgewinnung in Schlachthöfen' (Method of heat recovery in slaughterhouses). *Elektrowärme Int.* **34** (A5), A248–A250.

[41] Anon. (1982). 'Dishwasher with integral heat pump'. *J. Chart. Inst. Build. Serv.* **4** (6), 53.

[42] Griffith, M. V. (1957). 'Some aspects of heat pump operation in Great Britain'. *Proc. I.E.E.* **104A** (15), 262–78.

# Industrial applications

7

Industrial applications of heat pumps are specific both to the heat source, which may for example be an industrial warm-water effluent, and to the application of the heat to process or space heating. This being the case, an understanding of the general principles of heat pumping obtained from the previous chapters, together with knowledge of the specific case, should be all that is needed for the evaluation of industrial uses of heat pumps. A separate chapter devoted to industrial application should be superfluous.

Unfortunately this is not the case. Heat-pumping equipment suitable for industrial use has been available for some years but industry has been slow in starting to assess its applicability and in appreciating the value of energy savings which are possible in suitable applications. As recently as 1975 a major survey of efficient methods of energy use in industry prepared in collaboration with the Institute of Fuel and the UK Department of Energy was able to give heat pumping a cursory mention and a rapid dismissal [1]. However, recently published studies of heat recovery and drying applications using heat pumps suggest that worthwhile economic dividends allied to substantial primary energy savings may be obtained. It is, therefore, opportune to remind the reader of the scope for industrial utilization of heat pumps.

The period 1976–82 saw considerable growth in industrial heat pump applications, many of which were summarized in an international conference in early 1982 [2]. Ambient sources may be used for space heating of offices and similar buildings forming part of an industrial site using the techniques described in Chapters 5 and 6. Other applications of heat pumps in industry may be classified as follows:

(a) Recovery of process heat to provide space and water heating,
(b) Heat recovery from industrial effluents to provide process heating,
(c) Latent heat recovery as part of concentration or distillation processes,
(d) Drying of moist materials.

The use of ambient heat sources (air, ground-water, soil, etc.) for the provision of process heat is not likely to be suitable except in unusual circumstances. This is because process heat is generally required at relatively high temperatures and power requirements are usually too high for normal ambient sources to accommodate.

In general, heat pumps will be best suited to heat recovery applications in which latent heat forms a large proportion of the total heat to be recovered. Examples of each of these applications will be found below and further examples of the use of heat pumps in industrial heat recovery have been given by Reay (see bibliography). The most frequent applications to date have been in food processing industries, notably in dairy and brewing applications. An important source of heat for recovery has been waste heat from refrigeration equipment and the most frequent uses have been boiler feed water preheating, space heating, and drying. Sterilization and pasteurization are often required in conjunction with cooling, providing well-matched and long-duration heating and cooling requirements.

In all industrial applications it is important to match the supply of and the demand for heat as closely as possible, to attempt to avoid the expense of supplementary heat or thermal storage. It is also desirable to use equipment based on standard components and using well-proved techniques whenever possible.

To take full advantage of heat pumping it will frequently pay to alter the existing process to provide an overall optimal solution, rather than taking an existing process and seeing how a heat pump can fit into it. This point has been emphasized recently by an Austrian study in which eighty possible heat pump applications were considered and in which it was also concluded that potential applications should be sought first from the point of view of heat use, with the source a secondary consideration [3].

Examples of industrial applications of electrically driven heat pumps in specific areas are given below and some examples of fuel-fired units are considered separately. This is a somewhat artificial division but at present both fuel supply industries and governments tend to regard electric and fuel-fired heat pumps as quite distinct so that this division is convenient. One form of drive which falls between these categories is the steam turbine – if the process requires both high- and low-pressure steam, the use of a turbine expander between the pressure levels provides a potential source of drive power, and at least one application is being monitored in the UK [4].

## 7.1  Heat recovery to provide space and water heating

Steam and hot water requirements form a substantial part of the energy used by industry and much of this energy is eventually rejected as a warm water effluent. In the US for example, the annual provision of heat as process steam for use at temperatures not exceeding 110°C has been estimated at 670 GWh, some 3–4% of the total national energy use [5]. If heat pumps can recover heat from the effluent, there are clearly substantial energy savings which may be made.

Industrial processes often produce waste heat at moderately high temperatures, 50°C or above. Where this is the case, using the heat either directly or via heat exchangers is preferable to the added complexity of heat pumping, and this may be done effectively for space-heating purposes. Where the waste heat is at a lower temperature, heat pumping may be considered, especially where the process is more or less continuous when the factory is manned so that heat supply and requirement are synchronized.

A good example of the use of heat pumps to recover process heat is to be found at a plastics moulding factory at Telford, UK [6]. Traditionally such factories cool the moulding machines with chilled water from a cooling tower and there are problems of limited cooling capacity in summer and costs of appreciable evaporative water loss. At Telford these disadvantages were overcome and economical space heating was installed using a single water-chilling installation arranged as a heat pump. The chiller provides water at 7°C to the moulding machines and the water heated by the machines is passed to a large underground water storage tank. Heat extracted by the chiller (which is a standard item of refrigeration equipment) is circulated to fan-blown heat pump condensing units providing heat to the factory in winter, or to an alternative outdoor condenser circuit when the heat is not needed in summer. The amount of heat available is 325 kW.

In this example, not only is there a large saving in heating fuel costs but productivity and product quality are both improved due to steadier and lower cooling-water temperatures, water loss has been virtually eliminated, and heating-system safety has been increased following the replacement of fuel-fired units. There must be many other cases where improved cooling equipment would improve production in which the use of waste heat for space heating may be considered. A further example has been described by Fessel [7], in which ventilation heat recovery and water heating are also incorporated, using waste heat from glass-forming machinery.

## 7.2  Heat recovery to provide process heating

Occasionally there are processes in which heating and cooling or dehumidification are required simultaneously on a single production line and it is possible to pump heat directly from one part of the process to another. Production processes requiring the heating of the material prior to forming and its chilling after forming are obvious examples, and a further example is reported in which citrus-juice concentration and freezing are combined [8]. Usually heating and cooling requirements are less well-matched in both time and quantity and, if the waste heat is not available in excess, some thermal storage may be usefully incorporated in the heat pump system.

The output temperatures of available vapour compression refrigeration equipment are limited to a maximum of 90–110°C due to stability and lubrication limitations of established refrigerant fluids. As process-heat temperature requirements often exceed 100°C, the use of such heat pumps is not always possible. Nevertheless since the mid-1970s development of vapour-compression equipment suitable for higher temperatures has considerably widened the scope for obtaining process heat from heat pumps. At higher temperatures some processes are suited to 'open cycle' heat pumping which will be discussed in Section 7.3. In the future it is possible that fuel-fired heat pumps using engine exhaust heat recovery to boost output temperature will become technically attractive, and although their economics are at present unknown, they are being actively studied in a number of countries.

The first widely reported example of process heating by vapour compression heat pump is a pilot installation manufactured and used by Westinghouse at their transformer factory at Muncie, USA [5]. This system provides heat to treatment baths at 60°C and 77°C, using cooling water from electric seam-welding machines as a source, and incorporates thermal storage. A two-stage heat pump evaporating at 21°C and condensing at 93°C is used, in an arrangement illustrated schematically in Fig. 7.1. Output is 300–440 kW, depending on operating conditions, and the c.o.p. is typically around 3. The manufacturer has adopted the name 'Templifier,' an acronym from 'Temperature Amplifier', for this type of equipment. The thermal storage consists of a 150 m³ hot-water storage tank designed to provide 5 h standby heating when the welding machines are not operating. Electric resistance heaters are provided to give rapid start up and also provide both a standby emergency service and a capability for taking advantage of any off-peak electricity tariffs which might be offered.

This pilot installation appears to have been successful, as it led to the promotion of a range of 'Templifier' units from 63–291 kW input suitable for heat recovery from warm-water effluents. Heat exchanger and storage arrangements must be tailored to individual applications but the actual heat pumps can be limited to a small range of sizes. Performance is strongly dependent on the difference between source and sink temperatures, figures of 45–47% of the theoretical Carnot efficiency between these temperatures being claimed.

Two recent 'Templifier' installations in the dairy industry in Britain illustrate the flexibility of design which is possible with this equipment. In one which became operational in 1981 at Walsall, heat is available at 53°C in water leaving a milk cooler. This water flows through the evaporators of two separate heat pump units and returns to the cooler at 26°C, providing the necessary refrigeration for milk cooling. The two condensers are used to heat water available at 50°C to 70°C for space heating and boiler feed pre-heating. The overall c.o.p. is 5.7 and the output of 40 m³ h⁻¹ of water heated through 20°C (a heat output of 920 kW) is provided from an electrical input of 162 kW. Hot-water storage tanks are used to even out the differences between times of heat supply and demand.

A second installation at Bamber Bridge is illustrated in Fig. 7.2 and the basic heat pump circuits are outlined in Fig. 7.3. Two heat pumps are used with condensers in series and the two evaporators recover heat from separate sources. Chilled water is provided at 7°C and hot water at 60°C is supplied to boiler feed, caustic-tank heaters, and crate-washing equipment.

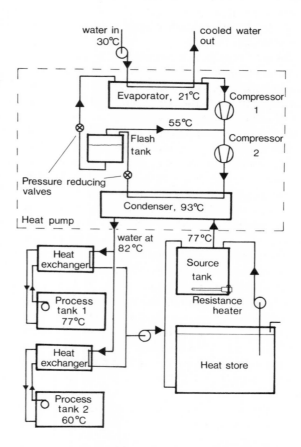

*Fig. 7.1* Layout of pilot installation of a 'Templifier' at Muncie.

*Fig. 7.2* Templifier heat pumps at the Milk Marketing Board dairy, Bamber Bridge. Courtesy of NEI Projects Ltd., sole UK distributors of the TPE range of Templifiers.

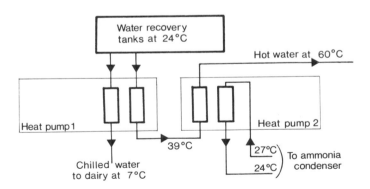

Water recovery tanks at 24°C

Hot water at 60°C

Heat pump 1

Heat pump 2

39°C

Chilled water to dairy at 7°C

27°C

24°C

To ammonia condenser

*Fig. 7.3* Bamber Bridge heat pumps, part of a complex water and heat recovery scheme.

The overall c.o.p. is 5.5, the heat output is 940 kW and the electrical input is 172 kW.

A proposal has been reported for a system in the French dairy industry in which chilled water at 2°C and hot water at 95°C are produced simultaneously using a two-stage cascade system [9]. This system, known as a 'Thermo refrigeration pump', links an R22 cycle condensing at 48°C with an R114 cycle evaporating at 43°C. On the low-temperature side, R22 evaporating at −2°C cools water from 5°C to 2°C, providing a cooling power of 84 kW for a compressor input of 36 kW. The R114 high temperature cycle condenses at 100°C and provides 121 kW to water heated from 90°C to 95°C and also 28 kW to a 60°C 'domestic' water supply. The high temperature compressor input is 38 kW, so the overall c.o.p. for heating is 2.01 with the bonus of considerable cooling.

As long as the hot and cold water demands are well matched for a long operating period such a system should be worthwhile. This particular system is expected to operate for many hours per year and an air-cooled auxilliary R22 condenser is incorporated to balance the system if cooling requirements predominate. The dairy industry is one in which simultaneous requirements for hot water and for cooling are common so increasing use of such systems is to be expected.

The main potential areas for the use of heat pumps to provide process heat are in those industries in which large quantities of water are used as part of the process such as the food and dairy industries, paper industry, textile treatment plants, chemical industries and in metal finishing, and increasing sales efforts from a number of manufacturers are expected. Anticipated payback periods of about 5 years have been quoted, without allowance for possible use of off-peak tariffs, tax concessions, or escalating fuel costs, and there are potentially large energy savings to be made. This would appear worth serious consideration by governments as a 5-year pay-back may be less attractive to the industrialist than the energy savings might be to an import conscious administration. Some form of economic incentive appropriate to the particular country may be necessary to encourage such energy saving.

## 7.3  Latent heat recovery for concentration and distillation of liquors

'Open-cycle' heat pumps, in which the refrigerant and the fluid being processed are the same, have been used in some industries for many years. This means of latent-heat recovery, commonly known as 'high temperature vapour recompression' or 'mechanical vapour recompression (MVR)' deserves wider consideration as a well-established technique with proven high efficiency [10]. In some countries this technique is beginning to be more widely adopted. In particular, in France the number of reported schemes has

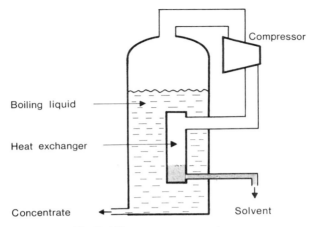

*Fig. 7.4* Vapour recompression.

increased from three to forty in the period 1980–82 [11].

The basic arrangement is shown in Fig. 7.4. Steam or other vapour is drawn from a concentration or distillation vessel and is compressed so that it may be condensed at a higher temperature. The high temperature condensation takes place in a heat exchanger within the vessel so that latent heat is returned to continue the process. The main product may be either the condensed liquid (as in a desalination or solvent recovery plant) or the concentrate. The technique is straightforward, of necessity the heat source and supply are well matched in both time and quantity (so long as there is a continuous feed of dilute solution), and as only small temperature differences are required a very high c.o.p. may be obtained. Applications are known in food processing, dairy, and chemical industries [12,13].

The temperature range over which the technique may be used depends on the acceptable range of temperatures and pressures for the product concerned. Compressor efficiences are likely to fall off rapidly at inlet pressures which are sub-atmospheric and, where water is the source, temperatures much below 100°C may not be economic. Table 7.1 shows how the boiling point of water and the specific volume of steam vary with pressure.

Of necessity the design of a vapour recompression heat pump will be an integral part of the design of a larger process plant. The requirement for large vapour volumes to be compressed through relatively small pressure ratios will favour centrifugal or turbine compressors, the specifications of which must be compatible with the working fluid and temperature. Possible applications must always be assessed relative to other heat recovery techniques and the simpler applications are likely to be the most successful. In straightforward liquor-thickening applications, a c.o.p. of 10 or more has

Table 7.1  Boiling point of water.

| Absolute pressure (bar) | 0.25 | 0.50 | 0.75 | 1.013 | 1.5 | 2 | 3 | 5 | 10 |
|---|---|---|---|---|---|---|---|---|---|
| Temperature (°C) | 65 | 81 | 92 | 100 | 111 | 120 | 134 | 152 | 180 |
| Specific volume (steam) ($m^3 kg^{-1}$) | 6.2 | 3.2 | 2.2 | 1.67 | 1.16 | 0.89 | 0.60 | 0.37 | 0.19 |

been achieved and water extraction rates of up to 22 kg $kWh^{-1}$ have been shown to be feasible [12]. Nevertheless, there is active research into other application areas including the drying of moist materials such as paper [14, 15].

An illustration of the application of vapour recompression to fluids other than water has been given by Martinon [16]. In this case heat is recovered in a fractional distillation column for aromatic hydrocarbons. Vapour is taken at 138°C from the head of the distillation column and is compressed and heated to 182°C to provide heat to maintain the base of the column at 170°C. The mechanical input to the compressor is 1.77 MW and the total system uses 5.5 times less power than would be required for a simple distillation process.

## 7.4 Drying

There are various ways of drying moist materials such as timber, plaster blocks, and paper, and it is often necessary to compare the efficiencies of different methods. A convenient parameter to use is 'effectiveness,' the amount of water extracted per unit energy input, expressed in $kgH_2O$ $kWh^{-1}$. The simplest drying method is to blow heated air over the moist material and to vent the moist air to atmosphere. This requires 3.6– 10 MJ (1–2.8 kWh) per kilogram of water extracted, an effectiveness of 0.36–1.0 $kgH_2O$ $kWh^{-1}$. An improvement is possible by recirculating a proportion of the air but the amount of improvement is limited and it is at the expense of increased drying time. As the latent heat of water is about 2.5 MJ $kg^{-1}$ and all the latent heat carried in the water vapour is lost there is clearly considerable scope for heat recovery.

One of the most efficient and controllable ways of drying moist materials is by using a closed dehumidifying chamber or kiln in which a heat pump is used to extract moisture. Water vapour is condensed and the latent heat is returned to the circulating air stream, using an arrangement such as that shown in Fig. 7.5. The temperature difference between evaporation and condensation is minimized by mixing the chilled air with air from the kiln

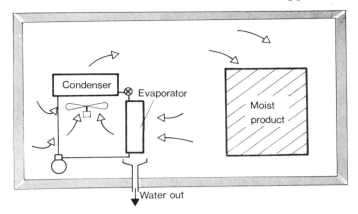

*Fig. 7.5* Dehumidified kiln using a heat pump.

before passing it across the condenser. This air mixing increases the c.o.p. of the heat pump and also reduces the highest temperature in the cycle.

Equipment suitable for kiln temperatures up to 50°C has been available for some years, one example being grain-drying equipment tested at the University of Minnesota in 1957 with a claimed effectiveness of up to 3.5 $kgH_2O$ $kWh^{-1}$ at 54°C [17]. Recent developments have extended temperatures to 80°C [18, 19]. It is planned to increase this further to 100°C above which it is envisaged that open-cycle steam recompression equipment as described in Section 7.3 might be used. An effectiveness of 3 $kgH_2O$ $kWh^{-1}$ has been reported which represents a primary energy saving of around 45% compared with existing dryers heated by steam produced from the combustion of fuel. Development is aimed at producing higher temperature equipment with an effectiveness of 4.5 $kgH_2O$ $kWh^{-1}$ and development work is reported to be required on refrigerant, lubrication, and evaporator design. The most widely quoted refrigerants for such applications are R114 and R12B1, the former being liable to condensation during compression and the latter suffering from high vapour temperatures. Work on lubricants must consider both stability and compatibility with refrigerant and other materials and improvements in evaporator design await the assembly of more accurate heat transfer data.

The rewards to be expected from this development work are appreciable. Potential energy savings for British industry have been surveyed by Hodgett [20] and similar studies have been published for other countries including Belgium and France [21, 22]. It is clear from these that there is already a substantial drying load which could be carried out by heat pumps and that this load will be increased considerably by the availability of equipment capable of working at temperatures up to 100°C. It seems probable that the first main result of higher temperature kilns will be to extend the range of products and materials which may be dried by this method. Improved efficiency in established areas of use should follow in the longer term once operating and control cycles have been fully assessed.

Timber drying is an application which has attracted considerable interest. In France nearly 1000 heat pump timber dryers were installed between 1970 and 1977 with an effectiveness of around 2 $kgH_2O$ $kWh^{-1}$ [22]. In Germany the dehumidified kilns operate at near ambient temperatures with drying times comparable to high-temperature conventional dryers but with energy use claimed to be reduced by up to a factor of 5 [23]. A Belgian study claims a comparable factor of around 3 using a heat pump optimized for use at 40°C [21]. The efficiency of a timber dryer is strongly dependent on the humidity in the kiln and on the moisture content of the timber and the figures quoted relate to the overall drying cycle. Detailed figures for particular instantaneous conditions have been presented by Geeraert [24] who quotes an overall effectiveness of 2.8 $kgH_2O$ $kWh^{-1}$ for drying oak from 40% to 9% moisture content in a kiln at 40°C. Higher temperature dehumidified kilns will give improved overall drying efficiencies. Careful control of the drying process is essential if a high-quality final product is to be maintained and control of heat losses from process equipment is necessary to maintain low energy use.

Drying by heat pump dehumidification may be applied to continuous processes using tunnel kilns requiring generally larger and more powerful equipment. Electricité de France have been involved in the assessment of tunnel dryers for building materials, and have a 216 kW pilot installation for the drying of plaster blocks [25]. This is designed to provide temperatures of up to 90°C and has been operated experimentally for several months. More complex tunnel dryers have been considered, including one combining air heating, high temperature vapour recompression, and closed cycle dehumidification in a single installation [15, 26].

In some drying applications, particularly those in which drying temperatures close to ambient are required, air recirculation may not be desired. Drying may then be achieved using a simple, open-cycle dryer with a heat pump providing latent-heat recovery, as shown in Fig. 7.6. In this case, heat is extracted from the moist exhaust air and is used to heat the incoming air. A grain-drying kiln working in this way was produced experimentally by Westinghouse, with an effectiveness of 2.2 $kgH_2O$ $kWh^{-1}$. A variation on this method was used in a French pilot plant in which a cool storage bin was linked to a dryer. The bin was used to chill grain to 4°C for storage and the dryer was heated to 50°C, heat being pumped from one to the other by a conventional heat pump using $2 \times 26$ kW compressors. The whole crop could be chilled rapidly and stored, and could then be dried in small batches.

Although all the drying processes referred to above relate to the drying of solid materials, this is not a necessary limitation. Heat pump dehumidifi-

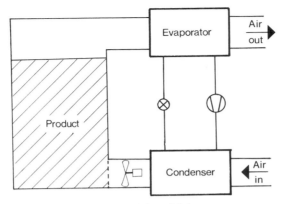

*Fig. 7.6* An open air drier with heat recovery.

cation may also be applied to the low-temperature concentration of liquids, including food products. In the concentration of orange juice for example, water evaporated from the juice is condensed at around 5°C and a heat pump is used to maintain the juice at 35–40°C. This method of liquid concentration may be considered whenever the maximum product temperature is too low for open-cycle vapour recompression to be effective.

Details of a number of specific applications of heat pumps to process drying have been recently published by a UK manufacturer who has worked in collaboration with the Electricity Council to increase the efficiency and operating temperature range of dehumidifiers, and increasing sales are to be expected [27].

## 7.5 Industrial fuel-fired heat pumps

Gas- or diesel-engine-driven heat pumps are generally more expensive and have a lower c.o.p. than electric heat pumps. The opportunities to incorporate engine waste-heat recovery and provide higher output temperatures can nevertheless make them competitive in some situations, although the economics of particular systems will be strongly dependent on the available fuel tariffs at the site.

The malting industry has a need for large quantities of heat and provides a steady demand over many hours of the year. Three British malt-drying kilns have or are having gas-engine-driven heat pumps installed. The earliest of these at Associated British Maltsters, Louth was commissioned in Spring 1981 and has a total rating of 3.5 MW. Heat is extracted from a 30°C humid exhaust-air stream and pumped up to 65–70°C to heat incoming air. Two twelve-cylinder engines drive two nine-cylinder compressors. The economics of this installation are being closely studied and the project attracted a 25% government grant as a demonstration project.

The same company is installing a 6.3 MW unit at Wallingford in which the engines drive both screw compressors and electricity generating equipment. At least one other company is following suit. Although these systems are presumably economic in terms of the heat produced, it is not known how they would compare with a recirculating dehumidified kiln such as is shown in Fig. 7.5.

Fuel-fired heat pumps are not limited to engine-driven vapour compression systems. A Japanese installation in a textile dyeing plant uses a gas-fired absorption system to provide hot water at 80°C with an output of 970 MW [28]. The claimed payback time for this installation is approximately three years. In the US, the Gas Research Institute is developing advanced vapour compression concepts for both open- and closed-cycle systems including rotary and turbine-driven centrifugal compressors [29]. Although existing technology has provided a number of fuel-fired units world-wide, there is considerable development effort being devoted to improved systems for the future.

## References

[1] Dryden, I. G. C. (Ed) (1975). *The efficient use of energy*. IPC, Guildford, UK.
[2] Stephens, H. S. and Jarvis, B. (Eds) (1982). *International Symposium on the Industrial Application of Heat Pumps*. Coventry, UK. BHRA Fluid Engineering, Cranfield, UK.
[3] Schnitzer, H. and Moser, F. (1982). 'Experience in the application of industrial heat pumps – conclusions from 80 case studies'. In *International Symposium on the Industrial Application of Heat Pumps*. Coventry, UK. BHRA Fluid Engineering, Cranfield, UK, pp. 117–28.
[4] Newbert, G. (1982). 'Industrial heat pump demonstrations'. In *International Symposium on the Industrial Application of Heat Pumps*. Coventry, UK. BHRA Fluid Engineering, Cranfield, UK, pp. 65–72.
[5] Szymanowski, H. W. (1975). *The heat pump for industrial processes – an overview*. Paper presented at Energy Conservation – A National Forum, Fort Lauderdale, Florida, December, 1975.
[6] Witt, J. A. (1976). 'Light industrial applications of heat pumps'. *Electrical Review* **198** (18), 26–7.
[7] Fessel, E. (1976). 'Ausnutzung der Albusstwärme in einem Glasverabeitungsbetrieb' (Waste heat utilization in glass processing). *Elektrowärme Int.* **34** (A5), A244–A247.
[8] Anon. (1950). 'Heat pumps effect savings in Florida citrus juice concentrating plant'. *Southern Power & Industry* **68** (8), 48–50.
[9] Lecrivain, E., Laroche, G. and Vallot, A. (1982). 'La production simultanée d'eau glacée et d'eau chaude à 95°C par une thermofrigo pompe d'une laiterie'. In *Refrigeration of Perishable Products for Distant Markets*, Conference at Hamilton, New Zealand, January 1982, paper 2, International Institute of Refrigeration, Paris.

[10] Hardy, W. E., Warne, D. F. and Griffith, M. V. (1976). *A technical and economic appraisal of mechanical vapour recompression.* ERA report 76–1023, Electrical Research Association, Leatherhead, UK.

[11] Degueurce, B. and Tersiguel, C. (1982). 'Problems encountered and results obtained in the application of compressors in industrial processes for energy conservation'. In *International Symposium on the Industrial Application of Heat Pumps*, Coventry, UK. BHRA Fluid Engineering, Cranfield, UK pp. 179–86.

[12] Peter, R. (1941). 'Heat pumps for evaporation'. *Escher Wyss News* XIV, 36–49.

[13] Baumann, A. (1948). 'A thermo-compressor installation for the concentration of milk'. *Air Treatment Engr.* 11 (9), 238–40.

[14] Justus, E. J. (1960). *Heat pump system for paper machine dryers.* US Patent 2 933 826.

[15] Laroche, M. and Solignac, M. (1976). 'Application de la pompe à chaleur au séchage dans les domaines agricoles et industriels' (Heat pump applications to drying in agricultural and industrial fields). *Revue Générale de Thermique* XV (179), 989–95.

[16] Martinon, J. (1976). 'Economies d'énergie dans les separations par distillation' (Power saving in separations by distilling out). *Revue Générale de Thermique* XV (179), 997–1001.

[17] Flikke, A. M., Cloud, H. A. and Hustrulid, A. (1957). 'Grain drying by heat pump'. *Agricultural Engineering* 38 (3), 592–7.

[18] Lawton, J., MacLaren, J. E. T. and Freshwater, D. C. (1977). 'Heat pumps in industrial processes'. pp. 47–56, in: *The rational use of energy*. The Watt Committee on Energy, London.

[19] Hodgett, D. L. (1977). *Dehumidifying evaporators for high temperature heat pumps.* Paper presented at International Institute of Refrigeration, Commissions B1, B2, E1, Belgrade, November 1977.

[20] Hodgett, D. L. (1976). *Improving the efficiency of drying using heat pumps.* ECRC/M956, Electricity Council Research Centre, Chester, UK.

[21] LABORELEC (1975). *La déshumidification de l'air et le sechage par pompe à chaleur* (Air dehumidification and drying by heat pump). Report 8. 1127.F.G2.BG.cr (April), LABORELEC, Belgium.

[22] Michel, H., Pottier, J. and Jaéglé, J. (1977). *Les pompes à chaleur à compression et à absorption – domaines d'emploi et perspectives de developpement* (Compression and absorption heat pumps – fields of use and future). Paper 4.6–1 presented at 10th World Energy Conference, Istanbul, September 1977.

[23] Fessel, E. (1974). 'Einsatz der Wärmepumpen zur wirtschaftlichen Holztrocknung' (Use of heat pumps for the efficient drying of wood). *Elektrowärme Int.* 32 (A4), A187–A191.

[24] Geeraert, B. (1976). 'Air drying by heat pumps with special reference to timber drying'. In: Camatini, E. and Kester, T. (1976). *Heat pumps and their contribution to energy conservation.* Noordhoff, Leyden, Netherlands. pp. 219–46.

[25] Bataille, M. (1977). *The first heat pump operated plaster block dryer.* Paper presented at Journées d'Informations Electro-Industrielles de l'Est, Strasbourg, November 1976. (Translated as O.A.Trans. 2146, Electricity Council, London.)

[26] Teculescu, N. (1977). 'Heat pumps for the drying of plaster blocks: economics and feasibility'. *PAC-Industrie* No. 5, 25–31. (Translated as O.A. Trans. 2173, Electricity Council, London.)

[27] Oliver, T. N. (1982). 'Process drying with a dehumidifying heat pump'. In *International Symposuim on the Industrial Application of Heat Pumps*, Coventry, UK. BHRA Fluid Engineering, Cranfield, UK, pp. 73–88.

[28] Kannoh, S. (1982). 'Heat recovery from warm waste water at dyeing process by absorption heat pump'. In *International Symposium on the Industrial Application of Heat Pumps*, Coventry, UK. BHRA Fluid Engineering, Cranfield, UK, pp. 129–41.

[29] Tabb, E. S. and Kearney, D. W. (1982). 'An overview of the industrial heat pump applications assessment and technology development programs of the Gas Research Institute, USA'. In *International Symposium on the Industrial Application of Heat Pumps*, Coventry, UK. BHRA Fluid Engineering, Cranfield, UK, pp. 169–78.

# Methods of economic analysis

# 8

If energy were plentiful and of negligible cost there would be no need for heat pumping to be used at all. However, energy has a restricted availability and an appreciable cost, and heat pumping can often reduce the energy requirements for a particular heating process. In general, heat pumps (and other types of energy conservation measures) offer reduced running costs in return for increased capital costs, and some way of balancing these factors must be sought in order to determine whether or not a particular application is wise. Economic analysis can be a tool to help people decide between alternative courses of action and as such is important in the assessment of heat pump applications.

## 8.1 Factors to be considered

In deciding to purchase any commodity the fundamental questions are 'Is it needed?' and 'Can it be afforded?'. A definite negative reply to either makes further analysis unnecessary. If some means of achieving the desired end is both needed and affordable then subjective or unquantified preferences may overrule further consideration and a decision may be taken. This is common in personal decision-making about the enjoyable trivia of life, such as clothing style or choice of holiday, but is usually considered unacceptable by managers or governments who have to justify their use of other people's resources. It is also insufficient for the individual householder who wishes to be sure of gaining maximum benefit from limited resources. What is now required is an answer to the question, 'Which of the alternative courses of action available will give the greatest benefit, relative to the costs involved?', and an answer is usually sought by comparing the options as monetary investments in a financial calculation.

In developing any method of economic analysis numerous factors must be considered. In comparing a heat pump with alternative equipment the alternatives must first be enumerated and the heat pump must be compared with the best of these. For domestic space heating in Britain the alternatives might be improved thermal insulation, off-peak electric heating, or gas-fired heating; in the US or France, direct electric heating may be an established alternative, and in many other countries oil-fired heating may be appropriate. An alternative which must be considered in heat-recovery applications is the use of simple heat exchangers. It may be necessary to consider new processes using heat pumps as well as the use of heat pumps in existing processes.

Having determined the alternatives to be compared the lifetimes of the equipment and their capital and running costs must be estimated. 'Lifetime' may be less than the physical lifetime either because anticipated maintenance costs for old equipment make replacement more attractive, or because the purchaser only expects to use the equipment for a limited time. Governments responsible for national resource allocation may be concerned with energy supplies 20 years hence but individuals may sometimes look less than 2 years ahead.

'Capital' cost includes both purchase and installation cost and may be offset by salvage value at the end of the 'lifetime'. 'Running' costs include present and future fuel costs, maintenance and insurance. All costs may be further complicated by taxation or by grants making their detailed assessment a complex matter. The way in which capital cost is included in the analysis will depend to some extent on whether or not borrowed money is used and on how important is the reduction of choice in how to use the capital. (It may be wise to maintain capital for future contingencies even if simple economic analysis suggests this is a poor investment.) Prediction of money inflation will influence the importance of capital costs, and fuel price inflation relative to general money inflation will influence the analysis of running costs. A detailed discussion of costs-in-use for buildings has been published by Stone [1].

As some of the factors in the analysis must depend on estimates of an unpredictable future, a 'sensitivity analysis', in which a range of values is taken and the range of results determined, is generally to be recommended. This is particularly important for applications in which a wide variability of use can be expected as in heating and cooling of shops. In this case energy use can vary considerably with variations in trading patterns and what is best in a given type of shop will depend on both the shop manager and on the type of goods sold. The individual owner must assess his own energy use relative to average values and those with a wider interest (manufacturer, utility, or government) must consider the full range of conditions over which the equipment may be operated.

## 8.2 Conventional analysis of cost-effectiveness

The basis of all conventional economic analysis is the assumption that money can be profitably invested. An investment of a sum of money now (say £100) will earn interest and be worth more later. Conversely, the worth of £100 now is more than £100 at a future date as now it has the potential to earn interest. (If a particular rate of interest is being used to calculate back to the present worth of a future sum the interest rate is known as the 'discount' rate.)

From this assumption methods of analysis for different types of investment and different methods of paying interest have been developed and may be found in standard textbooks. The method most commonly used to analyse the cost-effectiveness of investments is discounted cash flow (d.c.f.) analysis in which the present worth of a project is compared with the present worth of an alternative investment for an assumed discount rate [2]. The present worth of a future saving is calculated as follows. If the discount rate is $r$% per annum compounded, a saving of $s$ in $n$ years time has a present value $v$, where

$$v = s/(1 + r/100)^n.$$

If the saving is due to reduced energy costs, and the true cost of energy increases by $e$% per annum over other costs, this equation is modified to

$$v = s(1 + e/100)^n/(1 + r/100)^n.$$

The analysis may be carried out in one of two ways. A 'test discount rate' $r$ may be assumed, based on the known performance of alternative investments in the past and, using this, the total present worth of the future savings may be calculated. If the present worth of these savings exceeds the present worth of the cost, the proposed measure is regarded as 'cost-effective' or 'economic'. Alternatively, the total present worth of costs plus savings is taken as zero and the value of $r$ calculated to give a 'rate of return' for the measure which may be compared with alternatives. Value of $r$ and $e$ are those over and above any general level of monetary inflation which does not affect the analysis as it is assumed to affect all commodities equally.

Over the last few years, real rates of return on capital have been very variable. Negative values in the mid 1970s were replaced in the early 1980s by high positive values, particularly in the USA. In Britain, a test discount rate of 10% was used for some years as a rule-of-thumb index of acceptability for public investments. Market prices of index-linked investments in Britain in mid-1982 represent an expected rate of 2–3%, which is in line with long-term historic trends. Some of the implications of choice of discount rate will be considered later.

For business investments, the applicable discount rates need further adjustment to allow for the effects of tax concessions on investment, profits, property taxes, or whatever is relevant to the particular case. This not only complicates the analysis, it also makes the conclusions dependent on a greater number of unpredictable future trends.

In order to see clearly how these methods of analysis operate consider the very simple example of a small space-heating heat pump giving energy savings worth £20 annually compared with an alternative heating system. The present worth of the savings in each of 10 succeeding years are given in Table 8.1 for a range of discount rates. The figures show clearly that a high discount rate reduces the value of future savings very considerably and that the usefulness of discounted cash flow analysis as an aid to decision-making is strongly dependent on the choice of the appropriate discount rate. As future discount rates cannot be predicted the method has very limited value in assessing long-term projects. It may distinguish the possible from the impossible but cannot differentiate meaningfully between a range of possible and roughly equivalent options.

Although positive discount rates will be applicable for borrowed capital the individual with capital to invest may find a different situation. In Britain in recent years the average individual investing savings in a building society received interest at a rate 3–5% *less* that general monetary inflation, i.e. at a negative real interest rate. Although this may have been a temporary phenomenon it is interesting to see the effect of a negative interest rate on the example by Table 8.2. Here the discounting procedure works in reverse and future savings are seen to have a greater worth than present savings as present savings will depreciate in the intervening period. As a result investment now to give savings later appears very much more worthwhile. If a positive discount rate has been assumed over a period when real rates were negative, projects which looked uneconomic at all times in the past may be seen later as lost opportunities.

An economic evaluation of vapour compression heat pumps by O'Callaghan *et al.* [3] in 1976 using a 10% discount rate concluded that, compared with an oil-fired boiler, heat pumps for domestic use are not economic but that this result is very sensitive to the assumed capital cost of the heat pump. This analysis also shows that improved heat pump performance at the expense of a substantial cost increase is not worthwhile. An alternative and useful economic evaluation of domestic heat pumps has been carried out by Kernan and Brady [4]. Again the heat pump is compared with an oil-fired boiler but the results are presented as 'breakeven c.o.p.' for the heat pump for a range of additional capital costs, for 5% and 10% discount rates, and for constant or increasing oil prices. This analysis shows, for example, that a heat pump c.o.p. of 2.2 is economic if the heat pump costs no more than the boiler, oil prices are increased by 50% over 1975 levels, and a 5% discount rate is used. Alternatively a c.o.p. of 3.9 is necessary to justify a capital cost increase of £400 using a 10% discount rate and 1975 oil prices.

Table 8.1 Present value of a saving of £20 p.a. over 10 years (£).

| Discount rate (%) | Year | | | | | | | | | | Total |
|---|---|---|---|---|---|---|---|---|---|---|---|
| | 1 | 2 | 3 | 4 | 5 | 6 | 7 | 8 | 9 | 10 | |
| 0 | 20 | 20 | 20 | 20 | 20 | 20 | 20 | 20 | 20 | 20 | 200 |
| 2 | 19.61 | 19.22 | 18.85 | 18.48 | 18.11 | 17.76 | 17.41 | 17.07 | 16.74 | 16.41 | 179.66 |
| 5 | 19.05 | 18.14 | 17.28 | 16.45 | 15.67 | 14.92 | 14.21 | 13.54 | 12.89 | 12.28 | 154.43 |
| 10 | 18.18 | 16.53 | 15.03 | 13.66 | 12.42 | 11.29 | 10.26 | 9.33 | 8.48 | 7.71 | 122.89 |
| 20 | 16.67 | 13.89 | 11.57 | 9.65 | 8.04 | 6.70 | 5.58 | 4.65 | 3.88 | 3.23 | 83.86 |

Table 8.2 Present value of a saving of £20 p.a. over 10 years at negative discount rates (£).

| Discount rate (%) | Year | | | | | | | | | | Total |
|---|---|---|---|---|---|---|---|---|---|---|---|
| | 1 | 2 | 3 | 4 | 5 | 6 | 7 | 8 | 9 | 10 | |
| 0 | 20 | 20 | 20 | 20 | 20 | 20 | 20 | 20 | 20 | 20 | 200 |
| −2 | 20.41 | 20.82 | 21.25 | 21.68 | 22.13 | 22.58 | 23.04 | 23.51 | 23.99 | 24.48 | 223.89 |
| −5 | 21.05 | 22.16 | 23.33 | 24.55 | 25.85 | 27.21 | 28.64 | 30.15 | 31.73 | 33.40 | 268.07 |

A further parameter which may be used is the 'payback period' – the time taken before the worth of future savings adds up to the capital cost. For example, using data from Table 8.1, if an investment gave a saving of £20 p.a. and the capital cost was £150, then assuming a 5% discount rate the payback period would be a little under 10 years. This parameter is particularly useful for rapid comparative assessments of short-term projects, although it is sometimes used crudely to show that projects are not feasible. Ledermann [5] has assessed the combination of heat storage and heat pumps for space heating, obtaining payback periods of 14–37 years with a 5% discount rate.

'Simple' payback is the payback period calculated for a zero discount rate. The relation between simple and exact payback has been explored by Manian [6] who shows that simple payback is potentially misleading for periods exceeding about 5 years. An interesting application by Spielvogel [7] demonstrates that none of a wide range of solar-heating schemes is worthwhile, a conclusion which may be invalid if there are appreciable real increases in energy costs in the future.

A detailed US Department of Energy study of the economics of heat pumps and other residential heating and air-conditioning schemes is available [8] which provides much interesting material, including the effects of regional variations within the US. This particular study is recommended to the reader who wishes to examine conventional cost-effectiveness analysis in detail.

## 8.3 Energy analysis

Reading the published literature on heat pump applications one often finds statements to the effect that, although a particular application may not be 'economic', it is to be regarded as worthwhile. This, in fact, means that the method of economic analysis used is regarded as unsatisfactory or the chosen discount rate is regarded as too high but no alternative is being proposed. It is often felt that energy savings are not sufficiently highly valued in conventional analyses.

An alternative form of economic assessment is the use of energy rather than money as the basis of the analysis, in the belief that long-term economic values are better reflected by energy values than by current monetary values. The results of such methods have been entertainingly extrapolated to a fictitious society where energy and money correspond and the resultant values do have a certain appeal [9]. The methods of energy analysis are not unlike those of monetary analysis – both costs and savings are calculated in energy terms including costs of manufacture and transport. Labour costs are generally not included and a zero discount rate is usually used. A negative discount rate could be justified, on the grounds that energy is produced from diminishing natural resources. Energy analysis and monetary analysis yield different results, as has been demonstrated by Morris [10] in a study of housing-energy economics showing that the rank order of the alternatives considered is different for different analyses.

The basic assumption of energy analysis is that a unit of energy has a fixed value regardless of its source and its likely use. Thus 1 MJ in high-grade natural gas is equivalent to 1 MJ in low-grade coal or 1 MJ in timber. The fact that the timber could be used as a construction material for 70 years before being burnt, that the gas could be a chemical feedstock, or that the coal may be unusable other than in a very large power-station boiler, is considered irrelevant. Consequently energy analyses have led to differing opinions regarding their applicability [11, 12].

The need to refine energy analysis to allow for the non-interchangeability of energy sources was considered as long ago as 1946 by Faber [13], who suggested a modified unit of energy (the 'Carnot') in which 1 Btu available at temperature $T_1$ was equal to $(T_1 - T_2)/T_1$ Carnots relative to an arbitrary base temperature $T_2$. Using this system an infinite value of $T_1$ is taken for electricity but all other sources of energy are downgraded according to the proportion of the energy which can be converted to mechanical energy. Similar suggestions have been made by several authors but detailed analysis using this system has not found favour. It seems likely that rigorous energy analysis may be more complex than rigorous financial analysis and more prone to questioning.

## 8.4 Ranking systems

For long-term project assessment, discounted cash flow analysis can give any desired conclusion as long as there is freedom to choose a favourable discount rate. Conventional energy analysis is over-simplistic in its approach to alternative fuels. What then should the rational decision-maker do?

From the start it must be accepted that no analysis allows for all factors and any analysis can only give guidelines. Capital costs must be assessed in money terms, running costs may be assessed in either money or energy terms, and the balance between them is open to dispute. If a well-defined value can be attributed to a unit of energy then a conventional economic analysis is appropriate. If, however, the future cost of energy is regarded as an unknown quantity it is better for the purposes of any scheme simply to state costs and savings and leave the value judgements to the purchaser.

Economic analysis can provide a ranking order to aid in choosing from a range of projects, and a simple analysis with this aim in mind is worthwhile. For energy-saving projects Siviour [14] has suggested a simple ranking procedure using the annual energy saving per unit capital cost as a parameter. An alternative simple ranking procedure is the use of life-cycle costing – comparing the total annual capital and running costs averaged over the life of the equipment. A combination of these methods would seem worthwhile in which the parameter calculated is annual energy saving divided by average annual capital and maintenance cost over the life of the system. This parameter may be called 'the energy return' of the project.

As an example, consider the choice between a heat pump, solar heating, and much improved thermal insulation in a new single-family house, all as alternatives to a conventional heating system. Assuming for the sake of illustration that the costs in excess of those for a conventional system are as shown in Table 8.3, the comparison of the energy returns shows that insulation is the most effective investment, followed by the heat pump, followed by solar heating. Whether any or all of these is a worthwhile use of capital is a separate decision depending on availability of capital and its alternative uses for completely different purposes, and this decision cannot be made on economic analysis alone but requires wisdom and judgement in a much broader sense.

The energy return differs from conventional payback analysis in that no energy cost is assumed, so there is no attempt in the analysis to balance capital costs and energy costs. The final figure does indicate the energy price level at which such a balance will occur, but this is not its main purpose. The object is to show clearly which of a number of possible schemes will save most energy per unit of capital spent. It is particularly appropriate for comparing alternative energy-saving schemes with differing lifetimes.

Neither conventional economic analysis nor energy analysis is universally considered to give the 'right' method of choosing between energy saving options. A simple parameter such as the 'energy return' defined above may be more appropriate. Once this method has been used to determine the best energy-saving scheme it may then be compared with alternative financial investments using a conventional discount rate, although it must be appreciated that the choice of rate for this exercise may have a controlling effect on the outcome.

*Table 8.3* 'Energy returns' for alternative energy saving schemes in a new house

|  | Heat pump | Solar heating | Insulation |
|---|---|---|---|
| Installation cost, $C$ (£) | 400 | 700 | 400 |
| Annual maintenance cost, $M$ (£) | 20 | 10 | 0 |
| Lifetime, $L$ (years) | 15 | 15 | 40 |
| Annual energy saving, $E$ (kWh) | 7500 | 3250 | 9000 |
| Average annual capital and maintenance cost, $(M + C/L)$ (£) | 46.7 | 56.7 | 10 |
| Energy return, $E/(M + C/L)$ (kWh£$^{-1}$) | 160.6 | 57.3 | 900 |

As far as heat pumps are concerned, some applications are generally accepted, some are marginal, and some are clearly not economic. Improvements in performance and increases in fuel costs will widen the range of worthwhile applications, but only if these do not result in disproportionate increases in capital costs. Whether capital cost or performance is the limiting factor will vary between applications.

In making comparisons between systems, it is a mistake to regard the heat pump as an 'all or nothing' alternative. Frequently the best solution to a problem will be found by combining a heat pump with other measures. A good example is the use of heat pumps for space heating – in a building with poor thermal insulation a heat pump will reduce the heating energy requirement, but a combination of improved thermal insulation with a smaller heat pump can be more economic. Paradoxically, if the insulation is increased still further, the heating energy requirement could become low enough for the heat pump to be unnecessary, although for many buildings the cost of insulation to this stage would be unacceptable.

In some applications, such as industrial timber drying and swimming-pool hall dehumidification, the energy used by electrically operated heat pump systems can be so low that they compete effectively with all other established systems. In other applications, such as space heating using outdoor air as a heat source, the energy savings may or may not give cost savings depending on the local costs of alternative heating fuels. If energy costs increase relative to other costs then the number of economic applications of heat pumps will increase. In every case successful exploitation of heat pumps depends on correctly matching equipment to applications, including modifying the application itself where necessary and it is hoped that this book will make it easier to assess which applications are worthwhile.

## References

[1] Stone, P. A. (1967). *Building design evaluation – costs in use.* Spon, London.
[2] Building Research Establishment (1975). *Energy conservation: a study of energy consumption in buildings and possible means of saving energy in housing.* CP56/75, BRE Watford, UK.
[3] O'Callaghan, F., O'Kelly, M. E. J. and Wrafter, B. (1976). 'The economics of heat pumps'. *Technology Ireland* September, 13–15.
[4] Kernan, G. and Brady, J. (1977). 'Economic evaluation of heat pumps'. *Int. J. Energy Research* 1, 115–25.
[5] Ledermann, H. (1977). 'Space heating with heat pump and heat storage'. *Bulletin de l'Association Suisse des Electriciens* 68 (4), 185–7. (Translated as O.A. Trans. 2161, 1977, Electricity Council, London.)
[6] Manian, V. S. (1979). 'Towards an accurate view of payback'. *ASHRAE J.,* 21 (2), 28–30.
[7] Spielvogel, L. G. (1980). 'The solar bottom line'. *ASHRAE J.,* 22 (11), 38–40.
[8] Abbatiello, L. A., Nephew, E. A. and Ballou, M. L. (1981). *Performance and economics of the ACES and Alternative Residential Heating and Air*

*Conditioning Systems in 115 US Cities,* ORNL/CON–52, Oak Ridge National Laboratory, Tennessee, USA.

[9] Chapman, P. (1975). *Fuel's paradise: energy options for Britain.* Penguin, Harmondsworth, UK.

[10] Morris, E. N. (1978). 'Housing energy economics'. *Building and Environment* **13**, 11–19.

[11] Casper, D. A. (1976). 'A less-electric future?'. *Energy Policy* September, 191–211.

[12] Oplinger, J. L. (1975). 'Electric heating can save scarce fuels'. *Electrical World* **184** (8), 84–5.

[13] Faber, O. (1946). 'The value of heat with special reference to the heat pump'. *Proc. Inst. Mech. Engrs.* **154,** (September), 144–78.

[14] Siviour, J. B. (1977). *Ranking energy saving ideas.* ECRC/M1042, Electricity Council Research Centre, Chester, UK.

# Bibliography

**Textbooks**

The following English language textbooks are recommended.

*Heat pumps and refrigeration systems*

*ASHRAE Handbook and Product Directory:* 1978 (Applications), 1979 (Equipment), 1980 (Systems), 1981 (Fundamentals). American Society of Heating, Refrigerating and Air-Conditioning Engineers, Inc., New York.

*CIBS Guide*, Vol. A. (design data), Vol. B (installation and equipment data), Vol. C (reference data). Published as 35 separate booklet sections, Chartered Institute of Building Services, London, from 1974. (Replaces the former *IHVE Guide,* 1970.)

Ambrose, E. R. (1966). *Heat pumps and electric heating.* Wiley, New York.

Kemler, E. N. and Oglesby, S. (1950). *Heat pump applications.* McGraw-Hill, New York.

von Cube, H. L. and Steimle, F. (1981). *Heat pump technology.* Butterworth, London.

Armor, M. (1981). *Heat pumps and houses.* Prism Press, Dorchester.

Thevenot, R., translated by Fidler, J. C. (1979). *A history of refrigeration.* International Institute of Refrigeration, Paris.

Gosling, C. T. (1980). *Applied air conditioning and refrigeration,* 2nd edn. Applied Science, London.

Gosney, W. B. (1982). *Principles of refrigeration.* Cambridge University Press, Cambridge.

Rogers, G. F. C. and Mayhew, Y. R. (1969). *Engineering thermodynamics, work and heat transfer.* Longmans, Green, London.

*Solar heating*

Szokolay, S. V. (1975). *Solar energy and building.* The Architectural Press, London.
McVeigh, J. C. (1977). *Sun power.* Pergamon Press, Oxford.
Wozniak, S. J. (1979). *Solar heating systems for the UK: design, installation and economic aspects.* HMSO, London.

*Economic analysis*

Holland, F. A., Watson, F. A. and Wilkinson, J. K. (1974). *Introduction to process economics.* Wiley, London.

*Energy in buildings – conference proceedings*

Sheratt, A. F. C. (Ed) (1974). *Integrated environment in building design.* Applied Science, London.
Courtney, R. G. (Ed) (1976). *Energy conservation in the built environment.* The Construction Press/CIB, Lancaster, UK.

*Comfort*

McIntyre, D. A. (1980). *Indoor climate.* Applied Science, London.

*Stirling engines*

Walker, G. (1973). *Stirling cycle machines.* Clarendon Press, Oxford.
Walker, G. (1980). *Stirling engines.* Clarendon Press, Oxford.

*Industrial applications*

Reay, D. A. (1977) *Industrial energy conservation.* Pergamon Press, Oxford.
Reay, D. A. and MacMichael, D. B. A. (1979). *Heat pumps, design and applications.* Pergamon Press, Oxford.
'Industrial applications of heat pumps'. Symposium papers (1982), BHRA Fluid Engineering, Cranfield, Bedford, UK.

*Guides to equipment suppliers*

USA – ASHRAE handbook as above.
UK – *Refrigeration and Air Conditioning, Year Book.* (published annually). Maclaren on behalf of Refrigeration Press Ltd, Croydon.

Reay, D. A. (1981). *Heat recovery handbook*. Spon, London.
See also Loyd (1981) below.

**Literature surveys**

There have been a number of literature surveys relating specifically to heat
pumps, from which examples of various types of installation may be
found. The following list is not necessarily comprehensive.

Onslow, D. V. (1945). 'The heat pump for space heating'. Technical Report
Y/T7, BEAIRA, London, 89 refs.

Anon. (1967). 'The heat pump (1921–1966)'. Bibliography, IB 191A,
Electrical Research Association, Leatherhead. 302 refs.

Anon. (1973) 'Select list of references on heat pumps from 1960 to date'.
Bibliography B58, Electricity Council, London. 200 refs.

Anon. (1974). 'Heat pumps – select list of references June 1973–August
1974' Bibliography B98, Electricity Council, London. 55 refs.

Anon. (1977). 'Heat pumps – select list of references September 1974–
December 1976'. Bibliography B98a, Electricity Council, London. 108
refs.

Anon. (1981) 'Select list of references on heat pumps'. Bibliography B98c,
Electricity Council, London. 103 refs.

Loyd, S. (1981). 'The heat pump'. Bibliography LB 103/81, Building
Services Research and Information Association, Bracknell, UK. 505 refs,
plus 66 equipment suppliers.

Berridge, G. L. C. (1975). 'Heat pumps – key references in the literature'.
Brainchild Information Services, Boston Spa, UK. Approx. 600 refs,
1943–1974.

Anon. (1976). 'Solar energy – an annotated bibliography'. Property Services
Agency, Croydon, UK. Approx. 500 solar refs., including 8 to 'solar heat
pumps'.

Hundemann, A. S. (1981). 'Heat pumps, 1964–March 1981 (citations from
the NTIS data base)'. PB 81–805491. National Technical Information
Service, Springfield, Virginia. 333 refs. to US federally sponsored
research.

Hundemann, A. S. (1981). 'Heat pumps, 1978–March 1981 (citations from
the Engineering Index data base)'. PB 81–805509. National Technical
Information Service, Springfield, Virginia. 333 refs. to worldwide
literature.

**Journals**

The following journals carry a number of published papers relating to heat
pumps:

*ASHRAE Journal*
*ASHRAE Transactions*
*Electrical World (USA)*
*Elektrowärme International*
*Energy and Buildings*
*Energy Research (International Journal of)*
*International Institute of Refrigeration Bulletin* (mainly abstracts)
*International Journal of Refrigeration*
*International Building Services Abstracts*
*Proceedings of the Institute of Refrigeration*

# Index

Page numbers in **bold** type refer to chapter or section headings, and numbers in *italic* type are figure numbers.